Country

Tools

Essential

Hardware

&

Livery

FINDER'S GUIDE NUMBER SEVEN

Country

Tools

Essential
Hardware
&
Livery

FRED DAVIS

Library of Congress Card Number   74-29152
ISBN   0-914400-06-1

Drawings by Doug Moran

First Printing February 1975

Second Printing September 1975

OLIVER PRESS
1400 Ryan Creek Road
Willits, California 95490

CHARLES SCRIBNER'S SONS
New York

CONTENTS

INTRODUCTION

Whether farming on a large scale, on a modest homestead, or in a back yard, good tools are indispensable. The ground must be plowed, animals cared for, buildings put up, and countless other operations carried on in the day to day life in the country, all requiring tools.

This book is a guide to those tools which are rare or hard to find. Most are those which have been in use since the early homesteaders carved a place in the land. We have purposely avoided many power tools, concentrating on those which are hand powered or animal driven.

We have tried to include as many tools for which we could find suppliers. There are many others which are either no longer available or which we overlooked, and it is hoped that subsequent editions of this guide will correct any omissions or errors as may have occurred.

Very often, in the preparation of this book, we stopped looking for suppliers after we found one or two, even though we knew there were other major suppliers. Our purpose was to give you, the reader, at least one good lead as to where to buy the product. It was never our intention to comprehensively include each and every manufacturer or supplier, but rather to give attention to descriptions of the tools themselves.

COUNTRY TOOLS

ADZES

An iron or carbon steel instrument with an arching blade used to chip a fairly smooth surface on beams to create a beautiful surface for those open or exposed beam ceilings. It makes approximately a 4 inch cut. This old and venerable carpenter's tool takes a little getting used to, but the result is well worth the effort.

ADZE

Gibralter Equipment & Mfg. Co.
P.O. Box 304-K
Alton, Ill. 62002

Hubbard Tool Division
6305 Butler St.
Pittsburg, Pa. 15201

Mother's General Store Catalog
Box 506
Flat Rock, N.C. 28731

Kershaw Manufacturing Co.
P. O. Box 9328
Montgomery, Ala. 36108

Woodings-Verona Tool Works
Thomas St.
Verona, Pa. 15147

ALTERNATORS, PTO DRIVEN

What do you do when your electricity is out for long periods of time? Panic because your food freezer is thawing with a full load of expensive food? Not if you have a PTO driven alternator on hand. PTO means "power take-off" and is an "extra feature" available on most tractors. The PTO shaft on the tractor connects to the alternator. These alternator units can be portable or permanently installed, enabling you to use them wherever you need a supply of electricity: farm fields, woods, permanent house and summer or winter home—the range is endless.

PTO POWERED ALTERNATOR

Sears, Roebuck & Co.
925 South Doman Ave.
Chicago, Ill. 60607

ANTI-FREEZE
FOR CABIN TOILETS

I think Herter's found a winner when they came up with this product. It first creates a chuckle, but then the horrible thought of the expense of plumbing repairs resulting from a frozen toilet or drain pops into mind. It is also usable in any drain trap as well! They say it is harmless to septic tanks and won't kill the bacteria, and is good to 40 below zero.

ANTI FREEZE
FOR TOILETS

Herter's Inc.
Waseca, Minn. 56093

2

ANVILS

One thing a farrier (horseshoer) needs is an anvil to shape the

ANVIL

horseshoes. Also an anvil is very handy whenever a solid, heavy surface is needed to beat and shape a piece of metal. One thing for sure, once you've invested in one, it will take some time to wear it out.

Dixon, Williams Inc.
752 Washington Ave.
Carlstadt, N.J. 07072

Montgomery Ward & Co.
619 W. Chicago Ave.
Chicago, Ill. 60607

Hammel Riglander Co., Inc.
423-435 Hudson St.
New York, N.Y. 10014

Nasco
1524 Princeton Ave.
Modesto, Ca. 95352

Milwaukee Tool & Equipment Co., Inc.
2775 S. 29th St.
Milwaukee, Wis. 53246

APPLE PEELERS

These seem to be getting harder and harder to find. I can't think of a faster way to get one apple or several bushels peeled, cored and evenly sliced. Just think how much quicker putting up that supply of frozen, canned or dried apples will be. Fun to use, let the kids do it.

APPLE PEELER

Chief Products Co.
701 E. 59th
Los Angeles, Calif. 90001

Goodell Co.
Antrim, N.J.

3

Herter's Inc.
Waseca, Minn. 56093

F. B. Pease Co., Inc.
E. Henrietta & Jefferson
Rochester, N.Y. 14620

AUGER, EARTH/ICE/WOOD

This instrument is used for boring holes in earth, ice, wood or other soft substances. I have found augers that drill holes from 2 inches all the way up to 24 inches in diameter. Drill holes through the ice for that winter fishing, dig post holes, or even bore through tree stumps to make their removal easier.

AUGER

Gibralter Equipment & Mfg. Co.
P.O. Box 304-K
Alton, Ill. 62002

AUGER

H&L Tool Co.
Box 430-B
Montebello, Calif. 90640

Montgomery Ward & Co.
619 W. Chicago Ave.
Chicago, Ill. 60607

Herter's Inc. (earth & ice)
Waseca, Minn. 56093

Screw Conveyor Corp.
704 Hoffman St.
Hammond, Ind. 46320

AWLS, PIERCING AND STITCHING

Have you ever been camping and had your tent acquire a rip which let in the rain? Or had a piece of harness break and needed to pierce holes in it in order to repair it? An awl for stitching can be used to repair canvas, purses, belts, etc. The piercing type is very handy for leather work. These tools are quite inexpensive.

COLLAR AWL

4

AWLS, PIERCING & STITCHING (Cont'd)

Awl

W. H. Bagshaw Co., Inc.
25 Pine St.
Nashua, N.H. 03060

Herter's Inc. (stitcher)
Waseca, Minn. 56093

Robert A. Main & Sons
Tomley & Gaffle Rd.
Wycoff, N.J. 07481

C. S. Osborne & Co.
Warren St.
Harrison, N.J. 07029

USM Corporation
Dept. 28, 140 Federal St.
Boston, Mass. 02110

AXES

An important tool designed for hewing or chopping, etc. It has a head of iron or steel with a cutting edge and a handle. There are many types of axes made, the difference being in the shape and size of the head for the specific use to which the axe is to be put. It's hard to imagine a more basic country tool.

AXE

GOOSE WING
BROAD AXE

BROAD AXE

Buck Knives, Inc.
1717 N. Magnolia Ave.
El Cajon, Calif. 92021

Gander Mountain, Inc.
P.O. Box 248
Wilmot, Wis. 53192

Herter's Inc.
Waseca, Minn. 56093

Nasco
1524 Princeton Ave.
Modesto, Calif. 95352

Snow & Nealley Co.
Bangor, Me. 04401

AXE, BRUSH

An axe designed specifically for cutting brush. Supposedly
 safe than a machete and
able to cut through brush
and small trees up to 4
inches thick, although I
should imagine that would
depend on the strength of the person on the other end of
the handle. Some brush axes are made with replaceable blades.

Oley Tooling, Inc.
Oley, Pa. 19547

So-Rite Mfg. & Supply Co.
P.O. Box 6097
Raleigh, N.C. 27608

Nasco
1524 Princeton Ave.
Modesto, Calif. 95352

BAGS, BURLAP

What can be said about a burlap bag (or gunny sack) except
when you need one and can't find
it? Nothing else seems like it will do
instead. If I started listing the uses
for burlap bags (transporting live
fowl, or for use as foot wipers, or
for sand bags, or for feed storage, or .....) there wouldn't be
room for anything else in the book.

Alabama Bag & Burlap Co.
4330 Powell Ave. S.
Birmingham, Ala. 35222

Griedman Bag Co.
801 E. Commercial
Los Angeles, Calif. 90012

Augusta Bag & Burlap Co.
Augusta, Ga.

Sacramento Bag Mfg. Co.
530 Q St.
Sacramento, Ca. 95814

6

BARRELS, PINE/OAK

If you are a home wine maker of from 3 gallons to 50 gallons, pine or oak barrels are the thing for you. They are also useful  for soaking hams and bacon in salt brine, dry curing meats, or even for a corn mash if you have a little operation going on down in the hollow. If you are not a wine maker, there are scads of other uses for these barrels. Of course there are the logical people who would store things in them, but then there are those who would pad the tops and create beautiful stools suitable for the kitchen, bar or the playroom. One can also remove one end of a barrel, lay it on a stand, and have an instant dog house that looks really sharp. Tables and chairs can be created from barrels with a little ingenuity and work.

Cumberland General Store
Rt. 3 Box 479
Crossville, Tenn. 38555

Sears, Roebuck & Co.
925 S. Doman Ave.
Chicago, Ill. 60607

Herter's Inc.
Waseca, Minn. 56093

Spaulding & Frost & Co.
Fremont, N.H. 03044

Hussey Enterprises, Inc.
801 S. Ohio
Martinsville, Ind. 46151

Universal Container Corp.
540 Madison Ave.
New York, N.Y. 10022

BASKET, STEAK

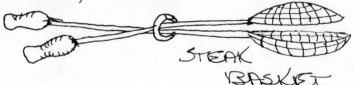

This is a really great little "tool." Generally when people see these, they think of juicy broiled steaks or hamburgers, but what some people don't realize is that you can cook fish, chops, sausages, ribs, chicken, hot dogs, etc. Really anything that can be clamped into it can be cooked with it. How about a tasty grilled cheese and tuna sandwich?

Cross Imports, Inc.
210 Hanover St.
Boston, Mass. 02113

Herter's Inc.
Waseca, Minn. 56093

BEAN POT & STAND, CAST IRON

Ever smell beans cooked all day over an open fire, or stew bubbly and hot with dumplings on top? This has to be a rare treat. Just such a stand and large-size cast iron pot is available. Even if you only plant flowers in it for a yard decoration, it has to be a great conversation piece.

Sears, Roebuck & Co.
925 S. Doman Ave.
Chicago, Ill. 60607

BEAR TRAPS

These are teeth-on-bar type traps that are the grandaddies
of the varmint traps used today.
They are a spring type trap and
illegal in many locations. Bear
invasions are not uncommon
in many parts of the country

BEAR TRAP

and if you have children, local judges tend to be lenient (but
no guarantees).

Gander Mountain, Inc.
P.O. Box 248
Wilmot, Wis. 53192

BEES/BEE KEEPING EQUIPMENT

These clever little insects of the order Hymenoptera are well

BEE KEEPING
EQUIPMENT

known world wide. The
honey producing types are
nature's best pollinators.
The regular honey bee we
are most familiar with has
one queen to a colony at a
time. She mates once in her
lifetime and lays a countless
number of eggs. A colony
can have thousands of
workers and a few hundred
drones. The lifespan of a

bee is about six weeks during the active season. Crop im-
provement, particularly in orchards, can be rapidly observed

with the help of these little fellows, to say nothing of the
value to you of their nutritious honey.

The Bee Hive
Dept. G. F.
Ojai, Calif. 93023

Sears, Roebuck & co.·
625 S. Doman Ave.
Chicago, Ill. 60607

Montgomery Ward & Co.
619 W. Chicago Ave.
Chicago, Ill. 60607

BELLOWS, HAND

Bellows have always held a fascination for me. They are usually formed of wood and leather with a metal tube or snout.
They are extremely useful in helping
get a fire blazing when it's first lit.
Some bellows are beautifully crafted
and are works of art. They can be
decoratively hung on the wall as well
as used practically. I should imagine

they would be a help in getting the charcoal going for a
barbeque as well as for use in the fireplace or wood burning
heater or stove.

Freeman Supply Co.
5720 Harvey Wilson Dr.
P.O. Box 15381
Houston, Tex. 77020

C.T. Moyse & Son
P.O. Box 228-T
East Rockaway, N.Y. 11518

Herter's Inc.
Waseca, Minn. 56093

BELLS, COW/GOAT/SHEEP/TURKEY

Bells have been used for centuries by shepherds, cattlemen, and others who keep animals.  When your livestock wander, it is much easier to locate them if you have them "belled." Also, you may be amazed to discover that you can distinguish your bells' sounds from others. It also helps you to know when some predator is scaring your livestock because of the noise the bells make. Some bells are actually tuned in harmony and make good wind chimes.

COW BELL

SHEEP BELL

Bevin Bros. Mfg. Co.	Mother's General Store Catalog
Bevin Rd.	Box 506
East Hampton, Conn. 06424	Flat Rock, N.C. 28731
John H. Graham & Co., Inc.	Nasco
617 Oradell Ave.	1524 Princeton Ave.
Oradell, N.J. 07649	Modesto, Calif. 95352

BELLS, FARM & SCHOOL MASTER'S

Bells such as these automatically set one back in time. There were bells on the large plantations and farms of early America. People got up, went to work, stopped work, were warned of danger, warned of fire, called to meetings, called to meals, etc., by bells. Bells are used by the United States Navy on the ships for signals to the crew. Bells were carried up

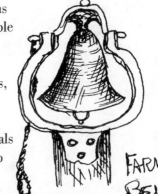

FARM BELL

11

BELLS

through California and installed in the early missions by the padres to call the people to worship. Lastly I mention the schoolmaster's bell. I'm sure there are many who remember the sinking sensation caused by the sound of the old school master's bell! Wouldn't it be great to have a bell to ring to call your kids in for supper?

Herter's Inc.
Waseca, Minn. 56093

Montgomery Ward & Co.
619 W. Chicago Ave.
Chicago, Ill. 60607

Sears, Roebuck & Co. (farm)
925 S. Doman Ave.
Chicago, Ill. 60607

BELL SCRAPER (HOG SCRAPER)

A device used for scraping the hair off a scalded pig. This hard-to-find little tool can save you many, many hours of work cleaning a pig before butchering. If you use this tool, you'll come to have a deep respect for it as I do.

HOG SCRAPER

Countryside General Store
Rt. 1, Box 239
Waterloo, Wis. 53594

BINS, GRAIN

If one has a large amount of grain to store, or wishes to hold grain for better selling prices, grain bins are the answer. They were made of wood years ago, but galvanized steel seems to be the material of today. These bins are particularly important if you don't want to pay the price of feeding half the county's mouse population.

GRAIN BIN

Graver Tank & Mfg. Co.
9200 E. Flair Dr.
El Monte, Ca. 91731

Ro-Mark Mfg. Co.
7009 Florin Perkins Rd.
Sacramento, Ca. 95828

Montgomery Ward & Co.
619 W. Chicago Ave.
Chicago, Ill. 60607

Sioux Steel Co.
1961/4 E. 6th St.
Sioux Falls, S.D. 57103

BIRDHOUSES

Not a real farm or country tool, but when you consider the help in eliminating insect pests that some breeds of birds do,

BIRD HOUSES

providing a shelter for the birds is profitable. Birdhouses come in a variety of shapes. They also come in "one bedroom" or the large apartment-size Martin houses. Of course you may instal the large size apartment house only to have a pair of birds stake a claim to the entire building! A few birdhouses scattered about the yard plus a bit of food should assure you of some of the best organic insect traps!

13

Herter's Inc.
Waseca, Minn. 56093

Montgomery Ward & Co.
619 W. Chicago Ave.
Chicago, Ill. 60607

Mother's General Store Catalog
Box 506
Flat Rock, N.C. 28731

Nasco
524 Princeton Ave.
Modesto, Ca. 95352

BOOT JACKS

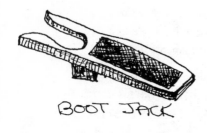

BOOT JACK

Getting a bit tired of pulling off your boots? This handy device made of wood or metal does the job for you. It is designed with an open end where where one puts the heel of the boot to be removed and the toe of the other foot on the closed end of the jack, forming a place to brace and loosen the boot for easy removal. Boot jacks come in several shapes and designs which make them attractive as well as practical.

J. F. Hodgkins Co.
Randolph
Gardiner, Me. 04345

Vulcan Corp.
6 E. 4th
Cincinnati, Ohio 45202

Mother's General Store Catalog
Box 506
Flat Rock, N.C. 28731

Weston Bowl Mill
Weston, Vt. 05161

BOTTLE CAPPER

A tool used to place crown caps on bottles and crimp them tightly. The cost of the bottle capper is almost immediately given back with the first using. Have you priced the cost of soft drinks and fruit juices lately? Think about "capping up" your own home brew, root beer and fruit juices. The bottle cappers adjust to fit almost any size bottles. Have a root beer making party—5 gallons of the brew can be made very rapidly and with lots of fun.

BOTTLE CAPPER

Continental Can Co., Inc.
Beverage Division
5745 E. River Rd.
Chicago, Ill. 60631

Everedy Co.
200 Monroe Ave.
Frederick, Md. 21701

Herter's Inc.
Waseca, Minn. 56093

BOTTLE CAPS

BOTTLE CAP

Very handy items to use with the bottle capper. Very practical if you want to keep something from coming out of the bottle into which you've put it!

Pancoast International Corp.
120-22 Liberty St.
New York, N.Y. 10006

United States Crown Corp.
100 Oak St.
Norwood, N.J. 07648

Sears, Roebuck & Co.
925 S. Doman Ave.
Chicago, Ill. 60607

BOTTLE CORKERS

Have you ever tried to put a cork into a bottle of wine you've
just racked without a bottle corker?
I have, and you can hurt yourself
doing it that way! This device is
made from wood or metal. The
lever type grips the bottle on both
sides, and when the levers are de-
pressed, the cork is inserted into
the bottle. The wood type needs
greater effort to operate but does
the same job as the lever type.

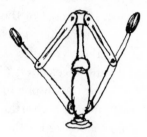

BOTTLE
CORKER

Worth the investment if you have several bottles to cork.

Mother's General Store Catalog
Box 506
Flat Rock, N.C. 28731

Presque Isle Wine Cellars
9449 Buffalo Rd.
North East, Pa. 16428

Sears, Roebuck & Co.
925 S. Doman Ave.
Chicago, Ill. 60607

Semplex of USA
4805 Lyndale Ave. N.
Minneapolis, Minn. 55412

BOTTLE CUTTER

This is a glass cutter set into a tool or holder which allows
you to cut almost anywhere on the bottle. There is an attach-

BOTTLE CUTTER

ment for one brand of bottle cutter
which, when used by hand, lets you even
cut holes in the bottle! The advantages
of owning a bottle cutter are endless.
We enjoy the free glasses, bowls and
cannister sets (lids can be purchased at
almost any thrift shop that will fit)
from all the bottles we used to just
throw away. You can make neat wind

chimes and hot caps from the cut tops too!

Bergen Arts & Crafts, Inc.
Box 38
Marblehead, Mass. 01945

BOTTLE CUTTER (Cont'd)

Bob's Arts & Crafts, Inc.
11880 N. Washington St.
Northglenn, Colo. 80233

The Handcrafters
1 W. Brown St.
Waupon, Wis. 53963

Herrschner's, Inc.
Hoover Rd.
Stevens Point, Wis. 54481

Maid of Scandinavia Co.
3244 Raleigh Ave.
Minneapolis, Minn. 55416

Mother's General Store Catalog
Box 506
Flat Rock, N.C. 28731

Pack-O-Fun
14 Main St.
Park Ridge, Ill. 60068

Sax Arts & Crafts
P.O. Box 2002
Milwaukee, Wis. 53201

Stained Glass Club
482 Tappan Rd.
Northvale, N.J. 07647

Village Candle & Craft
Box 486
Marshfield, Wis. 54449

BOTTLE LIFTER

Burned yourself lifting out those hot
jars or bottles during canning season?
This inexpensive little gadget enables
you to remove either empty or full hot
jars with ease. When you think of what
could happen when a jar of boiling hot
food is dropped, it makes the low cost
of the lifter even more attractive. Most
lifters can be operated with one hand.

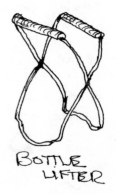

Mother's General Store Catalog
Box 506
Flat Rock, N.C. 28731

BOTTLE OPENERS

BOTTLE
OPENER

These used to be given away with almost every six-pack of soda pop or beer bought. Not any more, what with all the twist-off caps and pop-tops and throw-away bottles! So how is one supposed to open a can of milk? Well, there are still companies who manufacture the regular old fashioned bottle openers with the one end triangle-shaped (to open that can of milk) and the other end made to remove regular crown-type caps.

Brown & Bigelow
1286 University Ave.
St. Paul, Minn. 55104

Reliable Strainer Mfg. Co.
1725 N. Eastern Ave.
Los Angeles, Ca. 90032

Handy-Walden, Inc.
50-13 47th Ave.
Woodside, N.Y. 11377

BRANDING IRONS, HEAT/ELECTRIC/FREEZE

Hot irons used to imprint an identifying mark on an animal have been used for many years. There are the regular irons which are made of steel, copper or stainless steel and are heated in a fire, irons heated by LP gas or white gas, and electric irons. A bit different is the freeze type. This is the method where the iron is put in liquid nitrogen or dry ice and alcohol, and when touched to the hide of the animal kills the coloration (pigment) cells, making the hair grow in white instead of colored. One note

BRANDING
IRON

BRANDER

18

of interest: a brand increases in size as the animal does, so when choosing a brand, keep size in mind. Also, each state has its own laws governing the use of branding irons.

Everhot Mfg. Co.
Flothow & St. Charles
Maywood, Ill. 60153

Stone Mfg. & Supply Co.
1212 Kansas Ave.
Kansas City, Mo. 64127

Farnam Equipment
1167 Clinton St.
Buffalo, N.Y. 14240

Weston Mfg. & Supply Co.
P.O. Box 16297
Denver, Colo. 80216

Nasco
1524 Princeton Ave.
Modesto, Ca. 95352

White River Industries
915 Pine
Muskegon, Mich. 49440

BRIDLE BLINDS (BLINKERS)

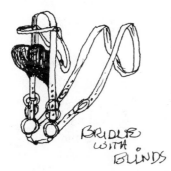

BRIDLE
WITH
BLINDS

A device fitting on either side of a horse's head, beside the eyes, that keeps the horse from being distracted or frightened by things beside him or coming up from behind.

Nasco
1524 Princeton Ave.
Modesto, Ca. 95352

Montgomery Ward & Co.
619 W. Chicago Ave.
Chicago, Ill. 60607

Sears, Roebuck & Co.
925 S. Doman Ave.
Chicago, Ill. 60607

BROODERS, CHICKEN — GAS/ELECTRIC/WOODBURNING

Brood chicks without a hen. A neat way to get a start in the chicken business. There are several types of brooders available, some brooding up to 400 chicks at once. Most of the electric ones seem to be thermostatically controlled and are quite dependable. The gas types are also thermostatically operated. The wood burn-

CHICKEN BROODERS

ing brooder is rather interesting, as it's not something one sees every day — and believe it or not, it also has a thermostat!

Nasco
1524 Princeton Ave.
Modesto, Ca. 95352

Robbins Incubator Co.
2555 S. Santa Fe Dr.
Denver, Col. 80223

Sears, Roebuck & Co.
925 S. Doman Ave.
Chicago, Ill. 60607

BRUSH CUTTER, MOTORIZED

Just about the most efficient and fastest way to clear brush and weeds. The motor-ized blade whirs through brush while you walk along. A sling worn over one shoulder supports the brush cutter. Great where speed is essential or the amount of brush would otherwise be overpowering.

BRUSH CUTTER

Montgomery Ward & Co.
619 W. Chicago Ave.
Chicago, Ill. 60607

20

BUCKBOARDS & CARTS

Want to save on gas? Get
yourself a buckboard or a
cart, a horse or a pony,
and off you go! You can
even attach jingle bells to
your harness for a delight-

ful ride. The horse carts can seat up to three adults. These
carts are well constructed and even have rubber-tired wheels.

Montgomery Ward & Co.
619 W. Chicago Ave.
Chicago, Ill. 60607

Nasco
1524 Princeton Ave.
Modesto, Ca. 95352

BUILDINGS, PORTABLE

If you need a building in a hurry, a well constructed portable

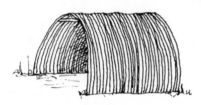

one may be the answer. These
buildings can be used for any
number of things. They make
really nice work shops, and of
course, great storage sheds.
They are generally constructed of aluminum or steel. It
is advised, though, that you

check the building codes where you live before getting too
enthusiastic, as local laws may restrict their use.

Montgomery Ward & Co.
619 W. Chicago Ave.
Chicago, Ill. 60607

Sears, Roebuck & Co.
925 S. Doman Ave.
Chicago, Ill. 60607

BUTCHER BLOCKS

It would be convenient if all kitchens automatically came with butcher blocks just like they come with sinks! These handy items are generally made of maple. They range in all sizes, even to table size on legs. The blocks can be built into your drain board or

BUTCHER BLOCK

island top with a knife rack along the edge. If you are remodeling, it would be a useful addition to your work area. Otherwise, smaller butcher blocks are available to be placed anywhere you're working.

Butcher Block & More
6100 S. Clinton St.
Chicago, Ill. 60616

Forrest Jones, Inc.
3274 Sacramento St.
San Francisco, Ca. 94115

BUTTER CHURNS

BUTTER CHURN (MANUAL)

There can't be any food much better than fresh, sweet, home-made butter dripping over hot biscuits (depending on your waistline and arteries!). There are several types of churns, all with the same principle—that being a paddle which churns the cream into butter, leaving buttermilk on the bottom of the churn. For those who want to really get back to the old ways, there are crock churns with a paddle on a stick which works like a plunger.

BUTTER CHURN

BUTTER CHURNS (Cont'd)

Delkor Industries, Inc.
Talmadge at 29th Ave, S.E.
Minneapolis, Minn. 55414

Mendocino County Farm Supply
2200 N. State St.
Ukiah, Ca. 95482

Sherrill Mfg. Co.
Rt. 5 Box 175
Cullman, Ala. 35055

CALF PULLER

If you've ever lost either a cow or calf from abnormal calving, this instrument could possibly have saved you both money and trouble. It is designed to aid in pulling the calf gently and safely during delivery, and with proper use will often prevent loss and injury.

CALF PULLER

Montgomery Ward & Co.
619 W. Chicago Ave.
Chicago, Ill. 60607

Nasco
1524 Princeton Ave.
Modesto, Ca. 95352

Weston Mfg. & Supply Co.
Box 16297
Denver, Col. 80216

CANNING KETTLES

These are designed to process canned food by the water bath  method. They also can be used as you would any large cooking pot, such as for spaghetti for a large crowd. The rack which fits into the pot holds several jars, the number depending on the size of the canner you get. I've seen them up to 9 quart size. They usually ly have an enamel or polished aluminum finish.

CANNING KETTLE

Oscar Krenz, Inc.
Ashby Ave. & 6th St.
Berkeley, Ca. 94710

Illinois Pure Aluminum Co.
109 Holmes
Lemont, Ill. 60439

Montgomery Ward
619 W. Chicago Ave.
Chicago, Ill. 60607

Mother's General Store Catalog
Box 506
Flat Rock, N.C. 28731

Paul Mueller Co.
P.O. Box 828
Springfield, Mo. 63101

Sears, Roebuck & Co.
925 S. Doman Ave.
Chicago, Ill. 60607

CAN SEALER

In this day and age of trying to find ways to economize, this has to be one of the better ways of doing so. Imagine canning your own tuna, salmon and vegetables in metal cans right in your own kitchen. Canned goods free from dents will keep indefinitely. Yours may not have the fancy colored labels that canned goods from the grocery have, but you will know what goes into the cans and have the satisfaction of doing it yourself.

Rowe Automatic Can Sealer
820 Saratoga Lane
Buffalo Grove, Ill. 60090

R & R Mill Co.
45 W. First North
Smithfield, Utah 84335

Scientific Filter & Machinery Co.
342 Canal St.
New York, N.Y. 10013

CASTRATORS

The practice of castration (removing the testicles of male animals) has been made easier in later years by the use of a rubber banding method. The instrument designed for putting the rubber bands in place can be operated by one man. The blood circulation is stopped, causing the testicles to become numb, atrophy and drop off. This method generally prevents the problems caused by bleeding, flies and screw worms.

CASTRATOR

Montgomery Ward & Co.
619 W. Chicago Ave.
Chicago, Ill. 60607

Sears, Roebuck & Co.
925 S. Doman Ave.
Chicago, Ill. 60607

Nasco
1524 Princeton Ave.
Modesto, Ca, 95352

Weston Mfg. & Supply Co.
Box 16297
Denver, Colo. 80216

CATTLE GUARDS

CATTLE GUARD

A device placed over a pit dug in the road where one would normally have a gate, thus preventing cattle, horses, sheep, etc., from getting out and eliminating the need for stopping to open a gate. Also, if your livestock tend to get out on the highway, this tool could save you from a rather nasty law suit.

Berstein Brothers Co.
100 N. Mechanic St.
Pueblo, Colo. 81003

Nasco
1524 Princeton Ave.
Modesto, Ca. 95352

CATTLE SCALE

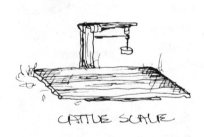

CATTLE SCALE

Either permanently installed or portable, these scales are really handy if you have a large herd. They can be used to check weight gain or for shipping purposes. Most scales weigh animals from 500 pounds up to 3,000 pounds.

Berstein Brothers Co.
100 N. Mechanic St.
Pueblo, Colo. 81003

Nasco
1524 Princeton Ave.
Modesto, Ca. 95352

Weston Mfg. & Supply Co.
Box 16297
Denver, Colo. 80216

CHAIN SAW FILES
& SHARPENER

A handy device that will save you time
and money. Quite simple to use and saves
you the hassle of taking your chain saw in
to be sharpened. Sharpener fits all chain
saws and adjusts to the proper angle for
filing. All you have to do is change the
diameters of the file to fit your size chain.

CHAIN SAW FILE

Montgomery Ward & Co.
619 W. Chicago Ave.
Chicago, III. 60607

Sears, Roebuck & CO.
925 S. Doman Ave.
Chicago, III. 60607

Nasco
1524 Princeton Ave.
Modesto, Ca. 95352

COFFEE MILL GRINDER

COFFEE GRINDER

Remember the smell of fresh
ground coffee? Now you can
grind your coffee as you need it,
rather than using pre-ground coffee.
It will taste fresher because it is fresher. There are table model coffee mills
or the larger size types. The grinder or
mill would allow you to try nearly
any coffee available, and even create
your own blends.

Bazaar de la Cuisine
1003 2nd Ave.
New York, N.Y. 10022

Braun North America
55 Cambridge Pkwy.
Cambridge, Mass. 02142

COFFEE MILL GRINDER (Cont'd)

Candle Mill Village
Peterbrook, Inc.
East Arlington, Vt. 05252

Cross Imports, Inc.
210 Hanover St.
Boston, Mass. 02113

Empire Coffee & Tea Co.
486 Ninth Ave.
New York, N.Y. 10028

Herter's Inc.
Waseca, Minn. 56093

Lekvar by the Barrel
968 Second Ave.
New York, N.Y. 10022

Maid of Scandinavia Co.
3244 Raleigh Ave.
Minneapolis, Minn. 55416

Manganaro's Food, Inc.
488 Ninth Ave.
New York, N.Y. 10028

Mother's General Store Catalog
Box 506
Flat Rock, N.C. 28731

Northwestern Coffee Mills
217 N. Broadway
Milwaukee, Wis. 53202

Paprikas Weiss Importer
1546 Second Ave.
New York, N.Y. 10022   10028

R & R Mill Co.
45 W. First North
Smithfield, Utah 84335

COME-ALONG

This tool has various names in different parts of the country, but anywhere this tool is used, its owner swears by it. It is really a modern version of the traditional block and tackle, and its uses are innumerable. Whether for pulling trucks and cars out of mud, sand or snow, or for pulling engines, or lifting barn corners, or pulling logs out of a creek, or pulling a stubborn mule into a pick-up truck, this tool can't be beat.

COME ALONG

Fairfield Industries, Inc.
336 Fairfield Rd.
Fairfield, N.J. 07006

Klein, Mathias & Sons, Inc.
7200 McCormick Rd.
Chicago, Ill. 60645

Sjogren Tool & Machine Co., Inc.
Auburn, Mass. 01501

COMPOSTING BINS

COMPOSTING BIN

These are economical "kits" made to be set up instantly to begin immedicte recycling of your leaves, grass cuttings, weeds, and all other organic wastes. With very little effort the rigid frame is set up and you can begin making rich compost for the garden and flower beds.

Montgomery Ward & Co.
619 W. Chicago Ave.
Chicago, Ill. 60607

Sears, Roebuck & Co.
925 S. Doman Ave.
Chicago, Ill. 60607

CONCRETE MIXERS

If you've quite a large amount of cement to be mixed and dread the effort of mixing it in a wheelbarrow, a cement mixer is what you need. I've found these handy helpers in sizes ranging from 2 cubic feet up to 8 cubic feet. They can often be rented, too!

CONCRETE MIXER

Berstein Brothers Co.
100 N. Mechanic St.
Pueblo, Colo. 81003

Nasco
1524 Princeton Ave.
Modesto, Ca. 95352

Montgomery Ward & Co.
619 W. Chicago Ave.
Chicago, Ill. 60607

Sears, Roebuck & Co.
925 S. Doman Ave.
Chicago, Ill. 60607

CORN PLANTERS

When you grow a greater amount of corn than a normal garden plot holds, a corn planter can be a great boon. These are of three types: hand, horse drawn, and tractor drawn. They place the corn in the rows at a specified distance apart, thereby eliminating loss due to spillage and excess waste, as well as speeding up the entire planting operation.

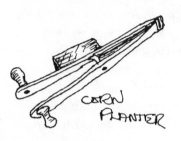
CORN PLANTER

John Blue Company (horse-drawn)
Laurinburg, N.C. 28352

Cole Mfg. Co.
1318 Central
Charlotte, N.C. 28205

CORN SHELLER/ WALNUT HULLER

A very complicated looking tool, but actually simple to use. Simply stick the ear of corn in the funnel shaped holder and turn the handle! You can shell (remove kernels) any dry ear of corn, including popcorn! Why not grow your own popcorn next year? You can also hull walnuts with some brands of corn shellers. There is also a corn sheller which is held in the hand rather than mounted on a table or bench, and is very inexpensive to purchase.

HAND CORN SHELLER

Decker Mfg. Co.
300 Blondeau St.
Keokuk, Iowa 52632

Durbin Durco, Inc.
1430 Woodson Rd.
St. Louis, Mo. 63132

Montgomery Ward & Co.
619 W. Chicago Ave.
Chicago, III. 60607

Nasco
1524 Princeton Ave.
Modesto, Ca. 95352

30

CORN SHELLER/WALNUT HULLER (Cont'd)

Sears, Roebuck & Co.
925 S. Doman Ave.
Chicago, Ill. 60607

The Shelby Mfg. Co.
400 Sigler St.
Sidney, Ohio 45365

COULTERS & SHARES, PLOW

The coulter is a sharp wheel or a sharp blade which is at-

tached to the plowbeam, and is used to slice or cut the the ground in advance of the plowshare. The plowshare is the broad iron or steel blade of a plow which cuts the ground at the bottom of the furrow. The plow's begin-

KNIFE COULTER

WHEEL COULTER

nings go back as far as the Bronze Age, or around 3500 B.C.

Osmundson Mfg. Co. (blade type)
Perry, Iowa 50220

Star Mfg. Co.
Carpentersville, Ill. 60110

Weise Corp. (plow share)
1501 Fifth St.
Perry, Iowa 50220

COUNTRY WINE ADDITIVE KIT

These kits are included just for fun, not necessarily for

necessity. The necessary part is up to you! The flavors offered sound too good to pass up! How about plum/ peach? Beet? Rhubarb? Others listed are banana, mead (honey), mint, raisin, orange, apple, strawberry (yum), cherry and

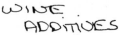

WINE ADDITIVES

dandelion. Each kit treats one gallon of wine.

Sears, Roebuck & Co.
925 Doman Ave.
Chicago, Ill. 60607

CREAM CANS

These cans can be used for the intended purpose of cream storage or can be adapted to many uses. They are generally made of bright tin plate and can be used to hold anything from flour to balls of yarn! The lid fits quite snugly, preventing contamination.

CREAM CAN

H. Behrens Mfg. Co.
471 W. Third St.
Winona, Minn. 55987

Mother's General Store Catalog
Box 506
Flat Rock, N.C. 28731

Bertels Metal Ware Co., Inc.
Rutter & Garner
Kingston, Pa. 18704

Montgomery Ward & Co.
619 W. Chicago Ave.
Chicago, Ill. 60607

Freund Can Co.
167 W. 84th St.
Chicago, Ill. 60620

Sears, Roebuck & Co.
925 S. Doman Ave.
Chicago, Ill. 60607

CREAM SEPARATORS

CREAM SEPERATOR

These ingenious devices allow you to really get more for your money from your milk. You may prefer or need skim milk for home use, and this device allows just such a use. Also you can separate your good cream for butter making and the like, and feed the skim milk to your hogs for a great boost in weight gain.

Cherry-Burrell Corp.
7515 N. Linder Ave.
Skokie, Ill. 60076

Wisner Mfg. Co.
1165 Globe Ave.
Mountainside, N.J. 07092

CROCKS

Fantastic things, crocks. There are crocks from the small tub type, known as rabbit crocks in our area and used for butter crocks in the mid-west, all the way up to the huge size large enough for an adult to fit in. They have thousands of uses, ranging from tanning or pickling to storing wool yarn, clothes or yard implements. Some crocks have dome-shaped lids, some flat lids; some have spigots for use as water or beverage containers. For making home-brew or wine, a crock is an absolute must.

CROCKS

Mendocino County Farm Supply
2200 N. State St.
Ukiah, Ca. 95482
  (UPS service only)

CROW BARS

Shaped like a cane with a flattened end, this heavy iron bar finds many uses about the farm. It has a claw on one end and is used for pulling nails or prying off boards. It is also useful for prying open painted shut or stuck windows, for raising sagging doors up to match the catch, and for many other purposes.

Brunner & Lay
9300 W. King
Franklin Park, Ill. 60131

Stanley Tools Div.
666 Myrtle St.
New Britain, Conn. 06053

Paragon Steel & Tool Co., Inc.
134 Rt. 20
East Rutherford, N.J. 07073

33

CUSPIDOR, BRASS

CUSPIDOR

Old timers may remember hanging around the saloon or general store, talking about the weather and crop prices. Chances are, there was a cuspidor or "spitoon" handy for the "chawers." Well, these are still around, and even non-chewers will find them useful as planters, storage pots, or just for looking at. As my neighbor says, there are two skills involved. One is learning to chew, the other is learning to hit the spitoon.

Miller Stockman
8500 Zuni, Box 5407
Denver, Colo. 80217

Mother's General Store Catalog
Box 506
Flat Rock, N.C. 28731

CULTIVATORS, HAND

No horse? Can't afford or don't have the room for a roto-tiller or tractor? A hand cultivator is your answer. This is a very useful tool for the money. Most come with a moldboard plow, a 5-pronged steel scratcher and a reversible steel shovel, enabling you to till enough ground to grow a garden. The large centered wheel makes it a smooth wheeling tool.

GARDEN CULTIVATOR

Montgomery Ward & Co.
619 W. Chicago Ave.
Chicago, Ill. 60607

Mother's General Store Catalog
Box 506
Flat Rock, N.C. 28731

Sears, Roebuck & Co.
925 S. Doman Ave.
Chicago, Ill. 60607

DAIRY SCALE

These very practical circular scales can be used to weigh about anything that can be put on a hook. They can normally hold up to 60 pounds. Most of them show both net and gross weights. Without one, it's awfully hard to tell how well your cow or goat is doing. The circular dial face is easy to read, and most seem to be moderately priced.

DAIRY SCALE

Douglas Homs Corp.
1542 Industrial Way
Belmont, Ca. 94002

Montgomery Ward & Co.
619 W. Chicago Ave.
Chicago, Ill. 60607

Ohaus Scale Corp.
35 Hanover Rd.
Florham Park, N.J. 07932

Nasco
1524 Princeton Ave.
Modesto, Ca. 95352

Sears, Roebuck & Co.
925 S. Doman Ave.
Chicago, Ill. 60607

DEHORNERS

If you have a problem and need to dehorn any livestock (sheep, goats or cattle), there are several devices with which you can do this. There is the rubber band dehorner, which looks like a pair of pliers and applies a rubber band to the horn base. Or there is the saw type, which saws the horn off at the base. And there is the electric type, which burns the horn off with 1,000 degrees of heat. Then there is dehorning paste, which is applied to the horn button of a young animal.

DEHORNER KIT

DEHORNERS (Cont'd)

Montgomery Ward
619 W. Chicago Ave.
Chicago, Ill. 60607

Sears, Roebuck & Co.
925 S. Doman Ave.
Chicago, Ill. 60607

Nasco
1524 Princeton Ave.
Modesto, Ca. 95352

DIGGER, POTATO

POTATO
DIGGER

This digger looks like a manure fork which someone stood on while pulling on the handle! It's bent at right angles from the handle, enabling the potatoes to be pulled to the surface. Handy whether you raise potatoes in your back yard or on a farm in Idaho.

Nasco
1524 Princeton Ave.
Modesto, Ca. 95352

DRIVE POINT

If you live in the part of the country with the proper soil conditions compatible to the use of a drive point, you can get water reasonably inexpensively by using one. One drives the point, with pipe added, to the depth required to obtain the water. The drive point is sharp at the end, and the small section above the point has perforations with screen around it, allowing the water to seep in. This drive point acts as a small well casing. A practical idea, and cheap, too!

Sears, Roebuck & Co.
925 S. Doman Ave.
Chicago, Ill. 60607

DRIVE
POINT

DUSTER, HAND OPERATED

A great way to dust or spray a small orchard or garden

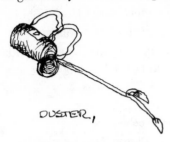

DUSTER,

with chemicals, insecticides or organic oil and pepper sprays. If you feel you should spray or dust your orchard for whatever reason, this is a very economical and man-hour saving way to go about it. The duster is supported by one or two shoulder straps. Some have nozzles on a flexible tube, while others have nozzles in a fixed position.

Nasco
1524 Princeton Ave.
Modesto, Ca. 95352

Sears, Roebuck & Co.
925 S. Doman Ave.
Chicago, Ill. 60607

EAR NOTCHER (HOG)

Another method used for identifying animals. This tool resembles a paper punch in design, with a spring between the handles. It comes in several shapes so as to allow for different notches. The three most popular are V-shape, keyhole shape and T-shape. There are several

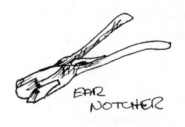

EAR
NOTCHER

numbering systems in use. Each breed registry has their own "approved" system.

Nasco
1524 Princeton Ave.
Modesto, Ca. 95352

Weston Mfg. & Supply Co.
Box 16297
Denver, Colo. 80216

EGG BASKET

EGG BASKET

These are quite well made and have a plastic coating covering the steel wire. They hold 15 dozen eggs and can be used for collecting eggs or fit in some egg washers. They would also make great baskets for holding fruit, etc., in the home.

Nasco
1524 Princeton Ave.
Modesto, Ca. 95352

Sears, Roebuck & Co.
925 S. Doman Ave.
Chicago, Ill. 60607

EGG CANDLERS

A device with which you can check eggs for staleness, blood clots, etc. This testing was originally done with a lit candle. One places the egg between the eye and the light, and thereby can see the quality of the egg.

EGG CANDLER

Lyon Electric Co.
3425 Hancock
P.O. Box 81303-B
San Diego, Ca. 92110

Nasco
1524 Princeton Ave.
Modesto, Ca. 95352

National Poultry Equipment
615 Wells Ave. N.
Renton, Wash. 98055

Sears, Roebuck & Co.
925 S. Doman Ave.
Chicago, Ill. 60607

Samuel Underberg Co.
620 Atlantic Ave.
Brooklyn, N.Y. 11217

EGG GRADER/SCALE

This little gadget is really easy to use. It weighs eggs so you can tell whether they are small, medium, large or extra large. A necessity if you market eggs, but it would be fun to have a grade your own eggs as it's not an expensive item to purchase.

Nasco
1524 Princeton Ave.
Modesto, Ca. 95352

Sears, Roebuck & Co.
925 S. Doman Ave.
Chicago, Ill. 60607

FARM JACK (4 TON CAPACITY)

Here is a tool that is amazingly versatile. It lifts, pushes, pulls, and can be used to form a suitable clevis for hoisting up to four tons! This has to be a help to the man doing work on the ranch or farm. The uses are endless, the investment is substantial.

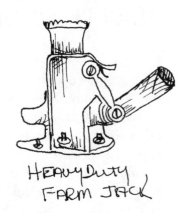

Berstein Brosthers Co.
100 N. Mechanic St.
Pueblo, Colo. 81003

FENCE POST DRIVER (MANUAL)

These handi-dandy, one man operated steel
post drivers range from inexpensive to quite
extravagant. I have to admit I don't think one
could drive and set a steel fence post without
one. These are operated by inserting the driver
over the post and lifting the driver and ram-
ming it down on the post, forcing it into the
ground. The ease with which the post goes into
the ground depends entirely on how hard the
ground is.

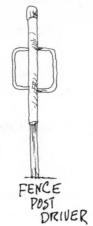

FENCE
POST
DRIVER

Berstein Brothers Co.
100 N. Mechanic St.
Pueblo, Colo. 81003

Montgomery Ward & Co.
619 W. Chicago Ave.
Chicago, Ill. 60607

Nasco
1524 Princeton Ave.
Modesto, Ca. 95352

Sears, Roebuck & Co.
925 S. Doman Ave.
Chicago, Ill. 60607

FENCER, 6 OR 12 VOLT, BATTERY OPERATED

Essential where an electric
fence is needed and no electricity is handy. Some charg-
ers have a 10 mile range while
others only cover up to three
miles. These fencers are great
around hog pens and for
general livestock control, but
another idea I've heard about

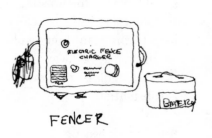

FENCER

is surrounding your garden and yard with an electric fence
which protects them from small animals.

Berstein Brothers Co.
100 N. Mechanic St.
Pueblo, Colo. 81003

Montgomery Ward & Co.
619 W. Chicago Ave.
Chicago, Ill. 60607

Nasco
1524 Princeton Ave.
Modesto, Ca. 95352

Sears, Roebuck & Co.
925 S. Doman Ave.
Chicago, Ill. 60607

Weston Mfg. & Supply. Co.
Box 16297
Denver, Colo. 80216

FERMENTATION LOCKS

This is really a quite simple device which fits into the bottle neck and allows the gasses to escape without allowing air to get in, which would turn your wine to vinegar. These are quite inexpensive and I honestly advise anyone to get one before attempting to make wine. Winemaking can be lots of fun, but imagine the disappointment of losing your vino due to it becoming vinegar.

FERMENTATION LOCKS

Herter's Inc.
Waseca, Minn. 56093

Lekvar by the Barrel
968 Second Ave.
New York, N.Y. 10022

Mother's General Store Catalog
Box 506
Flat Rock, N.C. 28731

Presque Isle Wine Cellars
9449 Buffalo Rd.
North East, Pa. 16428

Sears, Roebuck & Co.
925 S. Doman Ave.
Chicago, Ill. 60607

Semplex of USA
4805 Lyndale Ave. N.
Minneapolis, Minn. 55412

FILES/RASPS

This tool comes in many shapes and is quite a bit more versatile than one would imagine. One uses a file to remove part of something, for sharpening or smoothing a surface, etc. They come in a single cut file and many grades from smooth to very rough.

FILE

Herter's Inc.
Waseca, Minn. 56093

Nicholson File Co.
Providence, R.I.

Mother's General Store Catalog
Box 506
Flat Rock, N.C. 28731

Simonds Saw & Steel Div.
Interwale & Mack Rd.
Fitchburg, Mass. 01420

Nasco
1524 Princeton Ave.
Modesto, Ca. 95352

Titan Tool Supply Co, Inc.
66 Comet Ave.
Buffalo, N.Y. 14216

FIREPLACE GRILLS

If you use a fireplace, this gadget adds to the versatility of

FIREPLACE GRILL

the fireplace. People tend to forget that the fireplace was the source of heat, the cook stove, and, at times, the only light in the house. Having a grill means being able to barbeque even during the winter. These are designed several different ways and are worth looking into.

Portland Stove Foundry Co.
57 Kennebec
Portland, Me. 04101

FIREPLACE HANGER, SWING OUT

This fastens to the side of the fireplace, enabling one to hang a pot over the fire and cook many hot meals without using any other power source. There are some who say that there is no other way to cook stews, soups, etc.

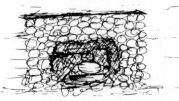

FIREPLACE HANGER

Sears, Roebuck & Co.
925 S. Doman Ave.
Chicago, Ill. 60607

FIREPLACE POPCORN POPPER

What's more fun on a cold winter's night than to make fresh

POPCORN POPPER

hot popcorn? Even if you might have other suggestions, making popcorn should at least be near the top of the list. With melted butter and mulled cider or wine it makes a nice way to spend an evening with friends, playing cards or just sitting around talking.

Corn Wall Corp.
500 Harrison Ave.
Boston, Mass. 02118

Cross Imports, Inc.
210 Hanover St.
Boston, Mass. 02113

Lekvar by the Barrel
968 Second Ave.
New York, N.Y. 10022

Wisconsin Cheese Makers Guild
6048 W. Beloit Rd.
Milwaukee, Wis. 53219

FIREPLACE TOOLS

These are usually comprised of a 4-piece set consisting of a stand or holder, broom, poker and shovel. Some larger, fancier sets include andirons and a wood basket or coal bucket. These sets are generally quite attractive as well as being useful. They are priced from moderately low to quite high, depending on your taste and pocketbook.

FIREPLACE TOOLS

Fred Meyer of Calif., Inc.
14 Park Ave.
Emeryville, Ca. 94608

Mission Foundry & Stove Works
544 Treat Ave.
San Francisco, Ca. 94110

Montgomery Ward & Co.
619 W. Chicago Ave.
Chicago, Ill. 60607

Sears, Roebuck & Co.
925 S. Doman Ave.
Chicago, Ill. 60607

Voos Cutlery, Inc.
101 Jermis St.
Cheshire, Conn. 06410

FISH BOIL KETTLE & STAND

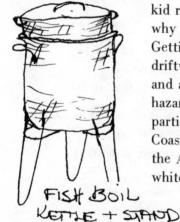

FISH BOIL KETTLE + STAND

I keep thinking about the fresh hot boiled crabs I ate as a kid right on the beach and wondering why this kettle wasn't around then. Getting a pot to balance on top of a driftwood fire wasn't all that easy, and a lot of boiling water can be a hazard if tipped over. The fresh crab parties I remember fit the Pacific Coast, but how about the lobsters of the Atlantic? Lake trout, salmon or whitefish can also be cooked in this kettle. This kettle has to be a winner because it can also be removed from the stand and used right in the kitchen on the stove as well.

Sears, Roebuck & Co.
925 S. Doman Ave.
Chicago, Ill. 60607

FLAT IRON (SAD IRON)

These are now rarely used to actually iron. Since the advent of gas and electricity, people rarely need to rely on sad irons. They can be used as door stops, bookends or just as an ornament. They are quite heavy as they are made from cast iron, and were heated by setting them on a stove or other heat source.

COMMON SAD IRON

Lodge Mfg. Co.
P.O. Box 380
South Pittsburg, Tenn. 37380

FLYPAPER ROLLS

Remember those little curliques of flypaper hanging from the ceiling all over the house when you were a little shaver? Well, here they are, and still available! Sure, I realize there are those nice little affairs that hang in a holder and kill "beasties" from the fumes they emit. They also have been banned from use in food preparation areas! These neat little flypaper rolls are the answer because they are perfectly safe and can be hung anywhere you've a need to eliminate

HANGING FLY CATCHERS

FLYPAPER ROLLS (Cont'd)

those buggy friends. Mother lists the active ingredients as rosin, rubber and mineral oil, and she also supplies a thumb-tack for hanging the strip!

Mother's General Store Catalog
Box 506
Flat Rock, N.C. 28731

FOOD DRYING RACKS

This rack looks quite attractive and well built, and uses the sun as the source of power to dehydrate the food. From a new book out in the summer of '74, I gather you can dry any kind of food if you prepare it properly for dry-ing. Dried fruit is becoming so expensive to buy that drying your own is a big money saver. On many homesteads, this is the only way garden produce is preserved throughout the winter.

Western Botanical Co.
710 Wilshire Blvd.
Santa Monica, Ca. 90401

FOOT SCRAPER

There are several shapes of foot scrapers and it sure saves getting hollered at if you remember to scrape the gook off your feet before walk-ing in on Mom's fresh scrubbed floor! These scrapers are generally made

FOOT SCRAPER (Cont'd)

from iron and can be placed right near the door for ready use, particularly after walking around in the pig pen all morning.

Montgomery Ward & Co.
619 W. Chicago Ave.
Chicago, Ill. 60607

Mother's General Store Catalog
Box 506
Flat Rock, N.C. 28731

FORCEPS

FORCEPS

A pincer-like instrument used for surgical purposes around livestock. They are used for grasping, compressing and pulling, and, as you can imagine, they come in a great many different sizes and

PIG FORCEPS

shapes. It doesn't take much ingenuity to find non-surgical uses for forceps.

Nasco
1524 Princeton Ave.
Modesto, Ca. 95352

Weston Mfg. & Supply Co.
Box 16297
Denver, Colo. 80216

FORGE

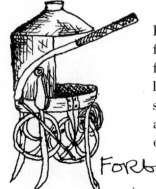

FORGE

Portable types are manufactured for home use on the ranch or farm. They are shaped something like a round barbeque pit on a stand and have a small hood and a hand-cranked air blower. You can use them to heat metal to be

shaped, to heat rivets, or to make any repairs around the
ranch or farm where a forge is required.

Atlas Rigging Supply Corp.
181-T Vanderpool St.
Newark, N.J. 07114

Champion Blower & Forge, Inc.
100 West Central Park
Roselle, Ill. 60172

Buffalo Forge Co.
465 Broadway
Buffalo, N.Y. 14204

Nasco
1524 Princeton Ave.
Modesto, Ca. 95352

FORK, MANURE

Used for cleaning cattle barns,
horse barns, sheep barns, etc.
It has five thin tines and is
approximately ten inches
wide and a foot long, not including the handle.

FORK, MANURE

Montgomery Ward & Co.
619 W. Chicago Ave.
Chicago, Ill. 60607

Nasco
1524 Princeton Ave.
Modesto, Ca. 95352

FROE

A type of cleaving knife having the blade and handle at
right angles. It is used for splitting off thin pieces of wood
such as clapboards or
shingles. This tool requires
some skill in getting the
hang of it, but if you lack
motivation, go down to
your local building supply
store and price roofing

FROE

48

materials. A froe, some proper wood and a little patience is a combination sure to prove invaluable.

Hubbard Tool Division
6305 Butler St.
Pittsburg, Pa. 15201

Mother's General Store Catalog
Box 506
Flat Rock, N.C. 28731

FRUIT CRUSHER

This device resembles nothing other than a box with the top wider than the bottom, resting on two boards with a chopping blade connected to a handle. If one made large amounts of jam or jelly, a fruit crusher would be a necessity.

FRUIT CRUSHER

Buffalo Hammer Mill Corp.
1243 McKinley Parkway
Buffalo, N.Y. 14218

Presque Isle Wine Cellars
9449 Buffalo Rd.
North East, Pa. 16428

Franklin Miller, Inc.
34 Meadow St.
East Orange, N.J. 07017

Semplex of USA
4805 Lyndale Ave. N.
Minneapolis, Minn. 55412

Thomas Mills Mfg. Co.
2182 Bennett Rd.
Philadelphia, Pa. 19116

Sears, Roebuck & Co.
925 S. Doman Ave.
Chicago, Ill. 60607

FRUIT PICKING BAG

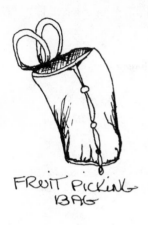

FRUIT PICKING BAG

I don't know how many times my wife has been the "catcher" at the bottom of the ladder while I was picking fruit. She doesn't always make the catch either. There never seems to be any place for the box to sit up in the tree to put the fruit in, hence the catching. I didn't know there was such a thing as a fruit picking bag all this time. It is worn over the shoulder, freeing both hands for picking fruit. Progress!!

L. F. Pease Co.
19 Grosvenor Ave.
East Providence, R.I. 02914

Townsend Mfg. Co., Inc.
Lake Wales, Fla. 33853

Riverside Tent & Awning Co., Inc.
3226 Franklin Ave.
Riverside, Ca. 92507

GARDEN TRACTOR

GARDEN TRACTOR

GARDEN TRACTOR (Cont'd)

These little tractors are really great for the small garden or larger yard. There are loads of attachments for them; snow blowers, spreader/seeders, lawn rollers, lawn aerators, and even a shredder attachment for making mulch, just to mention a few. For farming on a small scale and budget, one of these should seriously be considered.

Montgomery Ward & Co.
619 W. Chicago Ave.
Chicago, Ill. 60607

Sears, Roebuck & Co.
925 S. Doman Ave.
Chicago, Ill. 60607

GATE HARDWARE, BLACK STEEL

Black steel gate hardware really accents those great looking wood fences. Made of steel, these last ages (probably longer than the fence!). I should imagine you could use them other places as well as on gates and fences.

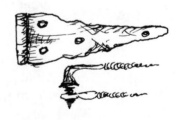

GATE HARDWARE

Montgomery Ward & Co.
619 W. Chicago Ave.
Chicago, Ill. 60607

Sears, Roebuck & Co.
925 S. Doman Ave.
Chicago, Ill. 60607

GLASS CUTTERS

GLASS
CUTTER

To replace a small window isn't such a chore, but if you've a bigger sheet of glass just sitting around, you could cut the smaller pane yourself and save money, as well as a trip to town. If you are a home hobbyist and work with glass, you definitely need a glass cutter. Very low priced and should pay for itself with the first using.

American Handicrafts
1312 Mission St.
San Francisco, Ca. 94103

GRAIN MILL

GRAIN MILL

Grind your own wheat into flour and then bake a loaf of bread! You can grind just about any grain (or nuts, etc.) you want. There is an electric kind or a hand operated kind;

MILL,
GRAIN

both fasten on the edge of the drainboard or table. Self-ground flour is not only economical but somehow better tasting than store bought. It certainly doesn't contain any preservatives.

Mother's General Store Catalog
Box 506
Flat Rock, N.C. 28731

Sears, Roebuck & Co.
925 S. Doman Ave.
Chicago, Ill. 60607

GRAIN SCOOP

A handy device for scoop-
ing out feed rations when
feeding your livestock.
Many are exact measure
sizes, enabling you to mix
your feed exactly accord-
ing to your requirements.

GRAIN SCOOPS

Mother's General Store Catalog
Box 506
Flat Rock, N.C. 28731

Nasco
1524 Princeton Ave.
Modesto, Ca. 95352

GREENHOUSES

In this day of high prices, I don't think one can say too
much about the uses of greenhouses. To many people, the

GREEN HOUSE

word greenhouse
just means flow-
ers and tropical
plants, but to
many others it
means winter
growing of vege-
tables and early spring starting of garden plants. Of course,
you can grow both flowers and vegetables if you juggle
your space around. One can have tomatoes year 'round, as
well as many other types of vegetables. Check into the cost
and advantages of owning your own greenhouse. You may
discover the costs are not as great as you thought and the
advantages greater than you imagined!

The Greenery
Box 489
Soquel, Ca. 95073

Handcrafted Wood
P.O. Box 425 S
Aptos, Ca. 95003

GREENHOUSES (Cont'd)

McGregor Greenhouses
Box 36510
Santa Cruz, Ca. 95063

Redfern Greenhouses
57 B Mt. Hermon Rd.
Scotts Valley, Ca. 95066

Pacific Coast Greenhouse Mfg. Co.
430 Hurlingame Ave.
Redwood City, Ca. 94063

Redwood Domes
Div SK
Aptos, Ca. 95003

Peter Reimuller, Greenhouseman
P.O. Box 2666 J10
Santa Cruz, Ca. 95063

GRILLS, BARBEQUE

If you haven't a barbeque grill, or haven't used one, check the possibility of getting one. Even hamburgers and hot dogs taste great, and if you look in any barbeque cookbook, especially James Beards', you will discover there are many things you can prepare on a barbeque grill that you wouldn't have thought possible. I especially like fish barbequed in a  lemon seasoned sauce wrapped in foil and done on the grill. Vegetables are really delicious prepared on the barbeque grill. They come in almost any size you can think of, and have spits, hoods, etc., available as well.

Herter's Inc.
Waseca, Minn. 56093

Paramount Wire Products
1035 Westminster Ave.
Alhambra, Ca. 91803

Rasmussen Iron Works, Inc.
12028 E. Philadelphia
Whittier, Ca. 90601

Simosen Metal Products Corp.
11600 W. King
Franklin Park, Ill. 60131

GRINDERS, MEAT

A food or meat grinder has to be one of the more handy tools one has in the home. You can grind everything from meat to fruit very successfully, and the initial cash outlay for the grinder isn't all that great. It takes so little effort to make your own lunchmeat and sandwich spread using a grinder, and then you know what's in the lunchmeat you're eating! These grinders are available in many sizes and types.

MEAT GRINDER

Bazaar de la Cuisine
1003 Second Ave.
New York, N.Y. 10022

Cross Imports, Inc.
210 Hanover St.
Boston, Mass. 02113

Homestead Industries
2014 Los Angeles Ave.
Berkeley, Ca. 94707

Homestead Industries
General Delivery
Argenta, B.C., Canada

Lekvar by the Barrel
968 Second Ave.
New York, N.Y. 10022

Mother's General Store Catalog
Box 506
Flat Rock, N.C. 28731

R & R Mill Co.
45 W. First North
Smithfield, Utah 84335

GRINDSTONES

GRINDSTONE

I haven't seen one of these for years. When you have big grinding or sharpening jobs to do, one of these is the

GRINDSTONES (Cont'd)

answer. I really doubt a person could wear one out in a lifetime. Therefore, this should be considered a pretty good buy.

Nasco
1524 Princeton Ave.
Modesto, Ca. 95352

HAIR CUTTING KITS

Once you get the hang of using one of these they are really great. You can save scads of money, besides feeling as though you have done something kind of special. My wife says that most of the women she knows who cut their husbands' hair take a special pride in saying, "I cut my husband's hair," or sons' or whoever. They may not realize they do this, but it's really something to be proud of. Most kits come with the clippers, several guides, a comb and scissors. Give several haircuts and you've paid for the kit! Remember, the only difference between a good haircut and a bad haircut is three days!

HAIR CUTTING Kit

Mother's General Store Catalog
Box 506
Flat Rock, N.C. 28731

Sears, Roebuck & Co.
925 S. Doman Ave.
Chicago, Ill. 60607

Montgomery Ward & Co.
619 W. Chicago Ave.
Chicago, Ill. 60607

HAMMERS, BALL PEEN

BALL PEEN
HAMMER

A rounded peen on a hammerhead used mostly in connection with a punch for riveting. There are several uses in metal working. They can be used to bend hot metal and also can be used for giving an antique effect to metal hinges, etc.

Montgomery Ward & Co.
619 W. Chicago Ave.
Chicago, Ill. 60607

Sears, Roebuck & Co.
925 S. Doman Ave.
Chicago, Ill. 60607

Nasco
1524 Princeton Ave.
Modesto, Ca. 95352

HAMMERS, MALLETS

MALLET

Mostly wood, these hammers are great for taking out dents from your truck fenders after backing up too fast into the loading ramp. Mallets are not for hitting nails. They are really a kind of shaper. An often-used tool.

Lixie Div.
P.O. Box 5048
Esmond, R.I. 02917

Metalspecialties, Inc.
1383 Kings Highway E.
Fairfield, Conn. 06430

Matticks Mfg. Co.
Matticks Bldg.
6415 E. Compton Blvd.
Paramount, Ca. 90723

Sears, Roebuck & Co.
925 S. Doman Ave.
Chicago, Ill. 60607

HAMMERS, SLEDGE

It's hard to describe how useful this super heavy, long handled hammer is. All the way from driving posts to humanely dispatching livestock, this tool is a must on any farm. It seems as though the heavier the hammer, the more useful it is.

HAMMER, SLEDGE

Gibralter Equipment & Mfg. Co.
P.O. Box 304K
Alton, Ill. 62002

Montgomery Ward & Co.
619 W. Chicago Ave.
Chicago, Ill. 60607

Portage Tool Co.
2675 Wingate at Cemetery
Akron, Ohio 44314

Sears, Roebuck & Co.
925 S. Doman Ave.
Chicago, Ill. 60607

Warren Tool Div.
P.O. Box 68
Hiram, Ohio 44234

HAND PUMPS

I have wanted one of these for years. A friend of ours has one and it's hard to keep away from it. I'm always getting drinks when I visit him. These are practical if you have no electricity, or a well in a location where it would be difficult to provide electricity.

HAND PUMP

Bernstein Bros., Inc.
100 N. Mechanic St.
Pueblo, Colo. 81003

Southwest Mfg. Co.
P.O. Box 722
Downey, Ca. 90241

U.S.M. Corporation
Dept. 28, 140 Federal St.
Boston, Mass. 02110

HAND SEED BROADCASTER

There are several kinds of seed sowers or broadcasters. This has to be better than crawling on your hands and knees or stooping or however you would ordinarily plant your garden! Now, the types for a home garden are a push type with two wheels. It has settings to plant seeds in small sizes, such as carrots, up to larger types, such as beans. The less expensive, smaller kind have one wheel with a straight handle.

HAND SEED SPREADER

To set the seed size you simply dial the seed you want to plant. These save seed and keep you from crowding the plants which require thinning. The other type of seeders are for sowing row crops, such as alfalfa clover, sudan, etc.

Nasco
1524 Princeton Ave.
Modesto, Ca. 95352

Sears, Roebuck & Co.
925 S. Doman Ave.
Chicago, Ill. 60607

HAND TRUCKS

HAND TRUCK

Ever had to borrow or rent a hand truck? Almost everyone has at one time or another. Do you have sacks of feed to carry around all the time, or bales of hay or alfalfa? I really hadn't thought one could easily buy such a thing, though I don't know why not! If you've lots of stuff to move and could use aid in doing it, a hand truck would be a big help!

Clinton Products
South Tecumseh Rd.
Clinton, Mich. 49236

The Fairbanks Co.
10 Glenwood Ave.
Binghamton, N.Y. 13902

Harper Trucks, Inc.
P.O. Box 33
Wichita, Kan. 67201

HARNESS, GOAT

A goat harness is used to attach a goat to a small cart. I've seen pictures of goats pulling small carts with one or two small children in them. Sounds fun! One thing for sure, it's not a pony harness. It's a very different thing.

GOAT HARNESS

Countryside General Store
Rt. 1, Box 239
Waterloo, Wis. 53594

HARNESS, HORSE/PONY

I have to admit I really know less about horse or pony harnesses than I do even about goat harnesses! It isn't something you see every day, but if prices keep getting any worse you will probably see a lot more. The harness is used to attach the horse or pony to the cart, buckboard, wagon or whatever. Some are really ornate, while others

BRIDLE

HARNESS, HORSE/PONY (Cont'd)

are quite plain. There are places where people make harnesses to your order, thereby allowing you to choose what is right for your needs.

Montgomery Ward & Co.
619 W. Chicago Ave.
Chicago, Ill. 60607

Nasco
1524 Princeton Ave.
Modesto, Ca. 95352

HARPOON (FOR HAY)

HARPOON
HAY FORK

Mostly used for picking up loose hay. The picture sort of describes itself. It is thrown or dropped into loose hay. When pulled, it catches large quantities of hay to be pulled up into the hay loft. Useful if you can't afford to bale your hay.

Chromaly American Corp.
160 Fifth Ave.
New York, N.Y. 10010

Metal Products Corp.
45 W. 19th St.
Weehawken, N.J. 07087

The Union Fork & Hoe Co.
500 Dublin Ave.
Columbus, Ohio 43215

HARROWS

There are several kinds of harrows made. The purpose of all, though, is the same—to level plowed ground. A harrow is usually a

HARROW

frame set with spikes or teeth. The quality of the seedbed prepared by harrowing can make a tremendous difference in your crops.

Nasco
1524 Princeton Ave.
Modesto, Ca. 95352

Sears, Roebuck & Co.
925 S. Doman Ave.
Chicago, Ill. 60607

HAY HOOKS

Many things come in pairs, and one would assume hay

hooks should too! Guess what, the ones I found don't! These look like a question mark with a handle! They enable even a child to move and drag down hay bales with ease. Once used, there is no other way.

Hay Hook

Mother's General Store Catalog
Box 506
Flat Rock, N.C. 28731

Nasco
1524 Princeton Ave.
Modesto, Ca. 95352

HAY SLING

This is a large size net which is placed in the bed of your hay wagon. After you have filled your wagon with loose hay and driven up to the barn, you simply pull up the net with a pulley and your hay is in the barn.

Hay Sling

Olson Mfg. Co.
620 S. Broadway
Albert Lea, Minn. 56007

HITCHING POST, HORSEHEAD

This is a really good looking tool which can really be used as a hitching post while being a beautiful yard ornament. Several of these would look fine along the drive or across the front of your yard. In some homes this may even be the perfect newel post inside the house.

Montgomery Ward & Co.
619 W. Chicago Ave.
Chicago, Ill. 60607

HORSE HEAD
HITCHING POST

HOBBLES

When you want to keep an animal, be it horse, cow, etc., from wandering off, you hobble it. A hobble is nothing but leather or metal circles which fit around the animal's two rear legs (usually) and are fastened together, keeping the animal from walking freely. Handy if you ride horseback out on a picnic and don't have a place where you can tether your horse, but can't let him run loose either.

Decker Mfg. Co.
300 Blondeau St.
Keokuk, Iowa 52632

Nasco
1524 Princeton Ave.
Modesto, Ca. 95352

Hastings equity Grain Bin Mfg. Co.
East Hastings, Neb. 68901

Wagner Specialty Co.
1647 Dodge
Burlington, Wis. 53105

HOG OILER, ROTARY

To help keep down, and in some cases prevent, parasites on pigs, a hog oiler is what is needed. Hogs like to scratch, and while they are satisfying an itch, the oil is spread on the hog, helping to prevent parasites.

Durbin Durco, Inc.
1430 Woodson Rd.
St. Louis, Mo. 63132

Fuller Mfg.
Centerville, Iowa 52544

Nasco
1524 Princeton Ave.
Modesto, Ca. 95352

Stone Mfg. & Supply Co.
1212 Kansas Ave.
Kansas City, Mo. 64127

Montgomery Ward & Co.
619 W. Chicago Ave.
Chicago, Ill. 60607

HOG RINGER

A kind of plier with slots in the nose of the pincers, to place the ring in, to enable the placing of the ring in a hog's nose. This helps prevent rooting done by hogs while slug, bug and root hunting.

Nasco
1524 Princeton Ave.
Modesto, Ca. 95352

Sears, Roebuck & Co.
925 S. Doman Ave.
Chicago, Ill. 60607

64

HOG WATERER, AUTOMATIC, HEATED

If you live in a part of the country where it gets cold and stays cold, this automatic heated waterer will keep the hogs drinking water even in the coldest weather. This has to be better than packing by hand when the pipes freeze.

HOG WATERER.

Montgomery Ward & Co.
619 W. Chicago Ave.
Chicago, Ill. 60607

HOISTS, HEAVY DUTY WAGON

HOIST

Montgomery Ward features these heavy duty wagon hoists. I didn't locate them anywhere else though there well may be some. There is a 5 ton size, 6 ton size, 7 ton size and a 10 ton size. These enable you to life 10, 12 and 14 foot wagon boxes.

Montgomery Ward & Co.
619 W. Chicago Ave.
Chicago, Ill. 60607

HOLDER, PIG

When you need to restrain your pigs for vaccinating, castration, ear marking or treatment of any
sort, a pig holder does the job for
you. There are at least six different
types of holders manufactured. Some
have the pig hanging head down and
some have the pig lying on its back.
In any case, not having to try holding
a 400 pound wiggling pig by hand
would be a relief for the large or small farmer.

HOLDER, PIG

Nasco
1524 Princeton Ave.
Modesto, Ca. 95352

Sears, Roebuck & Co.
925 S. Doman Ave.
Chicago, Ill. 60607

HOLDING CRATE, HOG

HOLDING CRATE, HOG

If you have any reason for
holding a large hog, either to
work on it or to move it, a
hog holding crate would certainly be a big help. Some
hogs, when they get to be of
a large size, also become dan-
gerous to handle by hand,
Some hog holding crates also
allow you to weigh the animal while confined.

Sears, Roebuck & Co.
925 S. Doman Ave.
Chicago, Ill. 60607

HOOF FILES, HORSE

When you put new shoes on a
horse you need to file down the
excess hoof to fit the shoes.
These files resemble a large rasp.

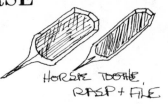

Mother's General Store Catalog
Box 506
Flat Rock, N.C. 28731

Sears, Roebuck & Co.
925 S. Doman Ave.
Chicago, Ill. 60607

Nasco
1524 Princeton Ave.
Modesto, Ca. 95352

HOOF PICKS

These are handy to carry with you when you're out riding
horseback. Sometimes a stone or other
foreign objects will get lodged in the bottom of your horse's hoof and hurt the
horse when pressure is put on the foot.
It's a bit like getting a rock in your shoe
and having to walk on it while carrying
a heavy object. This handy little tool
enables you to remove the object with ease.

Montgomery Ward & Co.
619 W. Chicago Ave.
Chicago, Ill. 60607

Sears, Roebuck & Co.
925 S. Doman Ave.
Chicago, Ill. 60607

Nasco
1524 Princeton Ave.
Modesto, Ca. 95352

HOOKAROON, AXE HANDLED

HOOKAROON

Stated as a tool that is good for handling post or pulpwood, etc. I've really no idea just what this tool is, but the name is interesting. There are names and there are names, but this name hookaroon has to be the greatest. Maybe you can get a better idea from the picture.

Nasco
1524 Princeton Ave.
Modesto, Ca. 95352

HOOK, BEAM

This is a hook resembling nothing more than a huge ice tong. Remember the ones the ice men used to carry? The prongs grip over a tree limb, barn beam, etc. It makes a portable support for a winch or a pulley— even a cow lift.

Nasco
1524 Princeton Ave.
Modesto, Ca. 95352

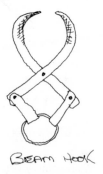

BEAM HOOK

HORSESHOE NAILS

As well as being useful for the purpose for which they were designed—holding on horseshoes—my wife says these pretty nails make really neat jewelry! Honestly! What they won't think of next! She says she has seen a type of collar necklace made from

HORSESHOE NAILS

HORSESHOE NAILS (Cont'd)

horseshoe nails that was really unique. I guess they would
make pretty earrings and bracelets as well, but I'd just as
soon shoe a horse with them.

Capewell Division
Stanadyne, Inc.
61 Governor St.
Hartford, Conn. 06106

HORSESHOEING EQUIPMENT

This equipment covers a very wide range of tools. Anvils,
horseshoe nails, hoof files and hoof picks have already been
covered. There are many
tools the horseshoer (farrier) uses to perform the
art of replacing horseshoes.
To name just a few of the
tools: shoe spreader, hoof

nipper, pritchel and a farrier's pincer. There are many things
to know about the art of horseshoeing which you can either
learn from a person already profound in this craft or there
are schools one can attend. There are also books which pro-
fess to be able to teach one to become a farrier.

Montgomery Ward & Co.
619 W. Chicago Ave.
Chicago, Ill. 60607

Sears, Roebuck & Co.
925 S. Doman Ave.
Chicago, Ill. 60607

Nasco
1524 Princeton Ave.
Modesto, Ca. 95352

Weston Mfg. & Supply Co.
Box 16297
Denver, Colo. 80216

HYDRAULIC RAMS

HYDRAULIC RAM

Not like any other pump, the hydraulic ram has a certain magical quality about it since it is powered by the water running into it, part of which it eventually pumps. A strange looking and sounding device, there are thousands in use throughout the country. They last forever (or so it seems).

Du-Well Mfg. Co.
W. Greenfield & S. 41st
Milwaukee, Wis. 53215

Rife Hydraulic Engine Mfg. Co.
Box 367-T
Millburn, N.J. 07041

Star Hydraulics, Inc.
2729 Clinton St.
River Grove, Ill. 60171

The Whole Mother Earth Waterworks
Green Spring, W. Va. 26722

ICE CREAM FREEZERS, MANUAL

Homemade ice cream! It's easy to make and lots of fun too! They start at a 4 quart size and go up to an 8 quart size. Some have poly tubs while some still have the wood tubs. It only takes about 20-25 minutes of cranking our 5 quart freezer to have luscious ice cream. There are so many kinds and flavors, you can make a new kind each week for a year and still not make

ICE CREAM MAKER

ICE CREAM FREEZERS (Cont'd)

the same one twice. There is even a tea flavored ice cream!
The one that surprised me was the rice ice cream!

Alaska Freezer Co, Inc.
Winchendon, Mass. 01475

J. E. Porter Co.
Ottawa, Ill. 61350

Mother's General Store Catalog
Box 506
Flat Rock, N.C. 28731

White Mountain Freezer Co.
Lincoln Ave.
Winchendon, Mass. 01475

ICE PICKS

These also used to be a "give away" item from ice and soda
works. This is no longer the case. When
we use our ice cream freezer, we use
our ice pick to break up the block of
ice which we place in chunks around
the freezer. The use of an ice pick is
much more than just chipping ice.
Piercing holes in almost anything (including your enemies) is one big help.

Acme Metal Goods Mfg. Co.
2 Orange St.
Newark, N.J. 07102

G. A. Burbridge Co.
1031 Richmond
Houston, Tex. 77006

W. H. Bagshaw Co., Inc.
25 Pine St.
Nashua, N.H. 03060

INCUBATORS

When hatching eggs without a hen, an incubator is what
one must use. There are sev-
eral different types of incubators. They all perform the
same duty, but are constructed of different materials and
are of different capacities.

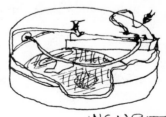

71

INCUBATORS (Cont'd)

There is one I read about which holds 1,200 chicken eggs, 3,100 quail eggs, 406 goose eggs, 800 turkey eggs, or 1,544 pheasant eggs. Then there is the very small size which holds two eggs for hatching. Custom hatching for feed stores and other retail outlets seems like a business where incubators of a large size would be used.

Montgomery Ward & Co.
619 W. Chicago Ave.
Chicago, Ill. 60607

Sears, Roebuck & Co.
925 S. Doman Ave.
Chicago, Ill. 60607

IRRIGATION SUPPLIES

To provide green feed for your livestock during dry weather or to irrigate your garden or pastures of alfalfa, sudan grass, etc., an irrigation system of some sort is needed. This usually entails getting the amount of irrigation pipe you require to cover the area you wish to irrigate. Then you get the sprinkler heads. There are timers which shut off and turn on the water at the times you specify. A good irrigation system does require thought and planning as well as a good water supply and usually an irrigation pump.

Nasco
1524 Princeton Ave.
Modesto, Ca. 95352

Sears, Roebuck & Co.
925 S. Doman Ave.
Chicago, Ill. 60607

KNIFE, CORN

This is a knife operated as one would a scyth to harvest corn stalks. For a small farm, the cost of a corn knife would be a much more logical choice rather than a more expensive tractor operation. It has an adjustable blade with a wood handle.

CORN SCRAPER

Nasco
1524 Princeton Ave.
Modesto, Ca. 95352

KRAUT SLICERS

Have you ever smelled sauerkraut fermenting and about half done? If you haven't smelled it, are you in for a sur-

CABBAGE
SLICER

prise! Phew! You won't actually forget it, let me tell you! Also it isn't exactly the smell one would want in the front room. But near the old wood heater isn't too bad a spot to get a place that has the proper temperature (70 degrees) required. The kraut slicer is the answer to not having nicked and sliced fingers. This gadget has a box where you place a half head of cabbage and slide the box back and forth across the cutting edges, thereby perfectly shredding the cabbage for sauerkraut.

Mother's General Store Catalog
Box 506
Flat Rock, N.C. 28731

LADY BUGS

The lady bug or ladybird is a member of the family Coccinellidae. The Australian lady bug was imported when a scale disease was destroying our citrus crop. The pretty little red bug with (or without) black spots is very beneficial to our gardens, be they flower or vegetable. The aphids which attack your brussel sprouts or roses are  no longer a problem when you have plenty of lady bugs. They are a key anti-pest tool used by organic gardeners.

Montgomery Ward & Co.
619 W. Chicago Ave.
Chicago, Ill. 60607

LAMP, HUDSON BAY HURRICANE

The design of this lamp hasn't changed in over 175 years. It burns any size candle, and even has a place in the base for the storage of matches! The base is made of either birdseye maple or of black walnut and the chimney is of triple thick glass for strength and durability.

Herter's Inc.
Waseca, Minn. 56093

LAMPS, KEROSENE

Many designs of kerosene lamps are on the market, and
they aren't hard to find. Most hardware stores and gift shops
have them. They come in colored or clear
glass, brass, etc. There are brackets which
enable you to hang them, or they may be
set on shelves or tables. They burn quite a
while on one fueling, depending, of course,
on the size of the receptacle holding the
kerosene. An interesting note—electric con-
verters are available for Aladdin lamps.
Therefore if you begin without any electricity and then either get a light plant (generator) or get electricity from an electric
company, you've not lost your investment in your lamp.

KEROSENE LAMP

Mother's General Store Catalog
Box 506
Flat Rock, N.C. 28731

LAMPS, CARBIDE

Mother's offers two types
of carbide lamps, the
heavy duty type or the
smaller mini hand type.
I don't know why sev-
eral of these wouldn't
do for patio or yard
lights. Mother's even has
the carbide crystals for
sale.

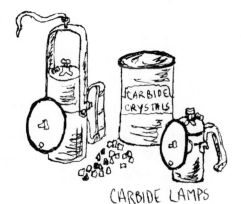

CARBIDE LAMPS

Mother's General Store Catalog
Box 506
Flat Rock, N.C. 28731

LEATHER TOOLS

LEATHER TOOLS

A great variety of leather tools are available. There are tools for both stamping and carving designs on leather. There are tools for punching holes and tools that cut leather into the shape you require. Leather working can be a fun hobby or a good business. You can make anything from hats to harnesses. Much more economical to make it yourself than to buy the finished product.

American Leather Co.
1609 Tampa St.
Tampa, Fla. 33601

Berman Leather Co.
147 South St.
Boston, Mass. 02111

Boin Arts & Crafts Co.
87 Mossis St.
Morristown, N.J. 07960

Cleveland Leather Co.
2824 Lorain Ave.
Cleveland, Ohio 44113

Colo Craft
1310 S. Broadway
Denver, Colo. 80210

The Hidden Village
215 Yale Ave.
Claremont, Ca. 91711

Indiana Leather & Supply
R.R. 2, Box 103
Bloomington, Ind. 47401

Kline, Savidge Co., Inc.
163 N. 3rd St.
Philadelphia, Pa. 19106

Mac Leather Co.
424 Broome St.
New York, N.Y. 10013

MacMillan Arts & Crafts, Inc.
9520 Baltimore Ave.
College Park, Md. 20740

MacPherson Bros.
730 Polk St.
San Francisco, Ca. 94109

Mother's General Store Catalog
Box 506
Flat Rock, N.C. 28731

Natural Leather
203 Bleeker St.
New York, N.Y. 10012

J. G. Read & Bros.
101 21st St.
Ogden, Utah 84401

LEATHER TOOLS (Cont'd)

S & S Arts & Crafts
Colchester, Conn. 06415

Sav-Mor Leather & Supply Corp.
1409 S. Los Angeles St.
Los Angeles, Ca. 90015

Sax Arts & Crafts
P.O. Box 2002
Milwaukee, Wis. 53201

M. Siegel Co., Inc.
186 South St.
Boston, Mass. 02111

Skil-Crafts Division
The Brown Leather Co.
205 Virginia Ave.
Joplin, Mo. 64801

S-T Leather Co.
329-33 E. Long St.
Columbus, Ohio 43215

Tandy Leather Co.
1001 Foch St.
Fort Worth, Tex. 76107

LIGHTNING RODS

These metal rods are attached to barns, houses or any building you wish to protect from being struck by lightning. There
is a wire which is attached to the lightning rod and then run
down into the ground, taking the electricity away from the
building.

Robbins Lightning Protection Co.
124-A East 2nd St.
Maryville, Mo. 64468

American Lightning Rod Co.
P.O. Box 82033
Lincoln, Neb. 68501

LIGHTNING RODS

LOOMS

There are many kinds of looms, many of which come in kit

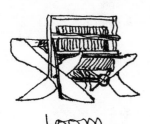

Loom

form for you to put together your-self. They can even be made from scratch if you are handy. You can make material, scarves, shawls, etc., on your own loom. I knew a gal who used dog hair and actually wove it into an article of clothing. The ideas are endless. There are so many things you can make and the loom can be quite sim-ple to operate with practice.

Ayotte's Designery
Box 287
Center Sandwich, N.H. 03227

Dick Blick Co.
P.O. Box 1267
Galesburg, Ill. 61401

The Handcrafters
1 W. Brown St.
Waupon, Wis. 53963

The Hidden Village
215 Yale Ave.
Claremont, Ca. 91711

House of Yarn & Crafts
Rt. 1, Lafayette Rd.
Seabrook, N.H. 03874

Kessenich
7463 Harwood Ave.
Wauwatosa, Wis. 53213

KM Yarn Co.
24065 W. Ten Mile Rd.
Southfield, Mich. 48075

Lily Mills Co.
P.O. Box 88
Shelby, N.C. 21850

The Salem Craftsmen's Guild
3 Alvin Place
Upper Montclair, N.J. 07043

Toijalan Kaidetchdas
PL 25
37801 Taijala
Finland

Tools of the Trade
R.F.D.
Fair Haven, Vt. 05743

The Unique
21½ E. Bijou
Colorado Springs, Colo. 80902

Varpa-Looms Ltd.
Osmontie 35
46800 Myllykooski
Finland

Weavers Corner Studios
P.O. Box 125
Kendall, Fla. 33156

LUMBER MAKING, CHAIN SAW ATTACHMENT FOR (ALASKA MILL)

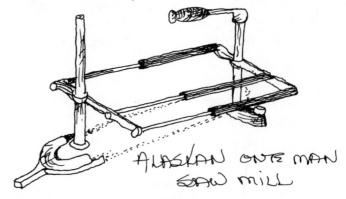

ALASKAN ONE MAN SAW MILL

This is a real nifty tool which makes boards and enables one man (or woman) to operate it. You can make boards from trees on your property, and if your building code allows it, you could build either a house, cabin, barn or shed with your own boards. I've seen houses built from boards made on this attachment and they were very professional looking.

Sears, Roebuck & Co.
925 S. Doman Ave.
Chicago, Ill. 60607

MATTOCK

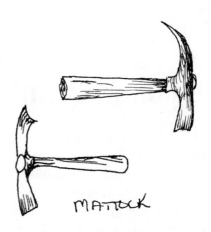

MATTOCK

The mattock is in constant use at our place. It is used for digging ditches, cleaning out ditches, making irrigation run-offs, breaking up ice,

MATTOCK (Cont'd)

dried manure, etc. It is a heavy tool and, if you can handle it, will put you in great shape.

Leetonia Tool Co.
Holt & Main Ave.
Leetonia, Ohio 44431

Woodings Verona Tool Works
1947 Thomas St.
Verona, Pa. 15147

Warwood Tool Co.
North 19th St.
Wheeling, W.Va. 26003

McLEOD

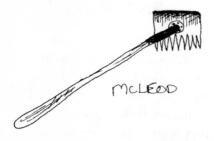

McLEOD

This is a U.S. Forest Service fire tool and is very effective and also darned heavy. Which may be why it is such an effective tool. It's a combination hoe and rake type tool. I've heard it is a very efficient brush clearing tool and if a person is either strong enough or trying to build up muscles, this is the tool for him.

Nasco
1524 Princeton Ave.
Modesto, Ca. 95352

MEASURING WHEEL, LAND

A useful device enabling one person to measure any firm or reasonably smooth land surface. Three types are manufactured to measure in feet, chains and meters. If you want to measure your pasture, walk it

MEASURING WHEEL

around the perimeter (no matter how irregular it is) the area is determined by finding the circumference and using the standard formula.

Nasco
1524 Princeton Ave.
Modesto, Ca. 95352

MEAT SAW, HAND

An invaluable tool for cutting meat, especially chops, but this is a great thing to own even if you don't cut meat! It can be used to saw winter squash and pumpkins in pieces suitable for cooking or paring for steaming as well as to saw

MEAT SAW

bone when cutting up lamb, deer, etc. My wife uses this handy saw to "slice" frozen home-made loaves of bread when she is caught short because she forgot to get out a loaf and there are lunches to be packed.

Atlantic Service Co., Inc.
711 Caton Ave.
Brooklyn, N.Y. 11218

Easy Speed Co.
1171 Folsom at Rodgers
San Francisco, Ca. 94103

International Edge Tool Co., Inc.
565 Eagle Rock Ave.
P.O. Box P
Roseland, N.J. 07068

MILK STRAINER

Rather than try drinking or pouring around those questionable "things" floating in your fresh milk, why not just invest in a small milk strainer? They are really worth it. There just isn't anything to using one; it's just a bowl-shaped thing with a strainer or a place for filters in the bottom and you simply pour

MILK
STRAINER

MILK STRAINER (Cont'd)

the milk in and it runs through leaving the crud in the strainer instead of the milk. Personally, I think it works great, but I hate washing the darn thing twice a day but one has to choose between "things" in your milk or clean milk.

Filpaco Industries, Inc.
3837 W. Lake St.
Chicago, Ill. 60624

Sears, Roebuck & Co.
925 S. Doman Ave.
Chicago, Ill. 60607

Louisville Tin & Stove Co.
737 S. 13th St.
Louisville, Ky. 40210

MOLDS, BUTTER

These allow you to have real pretty little pats of butter on your table for special occasions. It's a very inexpensive thing to purchase and it's fun to own one if for no other reason! You can get your initial or any number of decorative designs. They are usually made of wood. There are also the larger sized molds for half pounds or one pound. These are not especially decorative, but are nice to have.

BUTTER MOLD

Bogart & Hopper, Inc.
111 Charlotte Pl.
Englewood Cliffs, N.J. 07632

Metle-Pres Inc.
Foot of Commerce St.
Wilmington, Del. 19805

Cherry-Burrell Corp.
7515 N. Linden Ave.
Skokie, Ill. 60076

MUZZLES, WIRE (HORSE, COW, CALF, ETC.)

HORSE MUZZLE

Want to put your livestock in a pasture and restrict its feeding? Use a wire muzzle. These are particularly useful when you want to restrict an animal's diet and can be very helpful in restraining a bloated or foundering animal's natural grazing habits.

Worcester Wire Novelty Co., Inc.
111 Timonium Road West
Timonium, Md.

NEATSFOOT OIL

This handy oil is really great for waterproofing your boots for winter. It helps preserve leather and also helps to keep it soft. It is made from beef animal foot bones! Sounds wild but it is a good product and very helpful, unless you own a boot store!

Nasco
1524 Princeton Ave.
Modesto, Ca. 95352

NEATSFOOT OIL

NOSE BAGS

NOSE BAG

A canvas bag designed to fit over a horse's nose, providing a spill-proof dinner pail. Not wasting a grain in this day of high prices is an important factor! Right? This old fashioned device also allows several animals to be fed different diets simultaneously.

Atlanta Bag Co.
S. 5th St. & Union Ave.
Brooklyn, N.Y. 11211

A. Mamaux & Son
Mamaux Bldg.
Pittsburg, Pa.

NUTCRACKERS, CAST IRON/WOOD

NUT CRACKER

NUT CRACKER

These are often beautifully designed and would make an excellent gift for "that person who has everything" or the one who is so hard to buy for. There is a wooden one designed so that it slowly cracks the nut, thereby giving you more whole nutmeats. If you have a nut tree on your farm, there is no other way.

Grey Iron Casting Co.
P.O. Box 40
Wrightsville, Pa. 17368

Sears, Roebuck & Co.
925 S. Doman Ave.
Chicago, Ill. 60607

Montgomery Ward & Co.
619 W. Chicago Ave.
Chicago, Ill. 60607

Weston Bowl Mill
Weston, Vt. 05161

Arthur W. Reed Machine Co.
900 Thayer
Little Rock, Ark. 72202

OIL STONES

An oil stone is of a special type of stone very good for sharpening knives, clippers, etc. You put oil on the stone to keep the small openings in the stone from filling up with particles of metal. After you finish sharpening the dull tool,

OIL STONE

OIL STONES (Cont'd)

you should wash and dry your oil stone before putting it away. There are natural and artificial oil stones on the market. If properly cared for, one only need buy one oil stone in a lifetime.

Bay State Abrasives Div.
15 Union St.
Westborough, Mass. 01581

Waltham Grinding Wheel Co.
Waltham, Mass. 02154

Norton Company
50 New Bond St.
Worcester, Mass. 01606

PACK SADDLES

These are really handy if you are packing into the wilderness and have horses, donkeys or mules broken in to pack. These "saddles" aren't saddles at all in the sense one usually speaks of a saddle, but are specially designed to carry your gear, etc. Unless you have several "natives" to follow behind you and carry your gear on their heads, pack saddles are the thing.

PACK SADDLE

Mother's General Store
Box 506
Flat Rock, N.C. 28731

PAILS, MILK/DAIRY

Very handy for many uses as well as milk-
ing in. Most milk or dairy pails are made
of stainless steel or aluminum. I've found
them in capacities ranging from two quarts
all the way up to 16 quarts! The latter is
pretty heavy when filled. I discovered
that if they are properly washed and dried
they retain their shine and are beautiful
to handle and use.

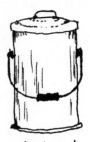

MILK PAIL

Montgomery Ward & Co.
619 W. Chicago Ave.
Chicago, Ill. 60607

Nasco
1524 Princeton Ave.
Modesto, Ca. 95352

Mother's General Store
Box 506
Flat Rock, N.C. 28731

Sears, Roebuck & Co.
925 S. Doman Ave.
Chicago, Ill. 60607

PEAVIES & CANTHOOKS

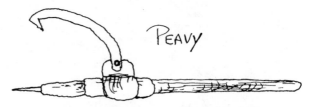

PEAVY

CANT HOOK

A peavy and canthook is a
harpoon-looking tool which
is used for rolling logs and
at the same time lifting them
a few inches so that your
saw will not hit the ground
or bind. Most peavies and canthooks use a moveable hook
which moves up and out to better grip the log.

PEAVIES & CANTHOOKS (Cont'd)

Leach Co.
2737 Harrison
Oshkosh, Wis. 54901

Snow & Nealley Co.
Bangor, Me. 04401

The Peaney Mfg. Co.
Box 371
Brewer, Me. 04412

PEELING BARS

This tool is intended for removing bark from trees before slabbing them into boards. As a country tool it is very useful. You can use it to break up soil, to start a post hole, as a lever for tightening fencing, etc. Without a doubt you will find many uses for a peeling bar once you've got one around the place.

PEELING BAR

Mendocino County Farm Supply
2200 N. State St.
Ukiah, Ca. 95482
(UPS service only)

PHONOGRAPH, BATTERY OPERATED

BATTERY OPERATED PHONOGRAPH

Not stereo or quadraphonic, maybe, but a phonograph usable without electricity. There are a couple of phonographs available. One plays 45's and 33 R.P.M. records, the other is a regular 3-speed! There are both sapphire and diamond needles available for them.

87

PHONOGRAPH, BATTERY OPERATED (cont'd)

Gander Mountain, Inc.
P.O. Box 248
Wilmot, Wis. 53192

Herter's Inc.
Waseca, Minn. 56093

PICKS

This is a handy tool when you are digging in hard or frozen ground or need to break up hard ground or ice for removal. It requires much energy and stamina to use.

Hubbard Tool Div.
6305 Butler
Pittsburg, Pa. 15201

Warwood Tool Co.
North 19th St.
Wheeling, W.Va. 26003

T. J. Miller & Co.
201 13th S.E.
Washington, D.C. 20003

PIPE THREADERS

Whenever you are putting in new pipe or replacing old, worn out or broken pipe, this would be a good tool to have around. This is one of those tools you don't require very often, but when you need one there isn't any other tool you can substitute. Having a pipe threader means you can cut pipe to size and thread it right on the job instead of having to take it to someone else to have it threaded. The best part is that you can use all the odd pieces of pipe laying around by cutting and threading them to fit the job you are doing.

Collins Machinery Corp.
951-55 Monterey Pass Rd.
Monterey Park, Ca. 91754

Toledo-Bever Tool Co.
1445 Summit St.
Toledo, Ohio 43604

Milwaukee Tool & Equipment Co., Inc.
2775 S. 29th St.
Milwaukee, Wis. 53215

PLANES, WOOD

WOOD PLANE

A tool used to smooth wood or shave it down in size, particularly useful in planing down a door to fit properly. This is a rectangle-shaped tool with cutting blades set approximately in the middle of its underside. One pushes the plane over the wood surface, thereby shaving off the wood in very thin strips.

BENCH PLANE

Fay & Egan Co.
2024 Eastern Ave.
Cincinnati, Ohio 45202

Nasco
1524 Princeton Ave.
Modesto, Ca. 95352

PLIERS, FENCE

These are a pair of pliers with added attractions or accessories built right on. They are shaped like a hammer on one side of the "head"—in fact this is a hammer! The other side of the head is shaped like a pick, only smaller sized, and is quite handy. The center of the head, made to be used for twisting wire, does a

FENCE TOOL

PLIERS, FENCE (Cont'd)

good job quickly and easily too. On both sides at about where the "neck" would be are wire cutters. These are good for cutting fence or baling wire but not very fine wire. In between the handles up near the neck is a grid type pattern stamped in the metal for gripping.

Montgomery Ward & Co.
619 W. Chicago Ave.
Chicago, Ill. 60607

Sears, Roebuck & Co.
925 S. Doman Ave.
Chicago, Ill. 60607

Nasco
1524 Princeton Ave.
Modesto, Ca. 95352

PLIERS, GENERAL PURPOSE

Pliers are something every farmer should have just as one owns a hammer or a pair of scissors. Whenever you need to grasp and hold an object, such as a nut while you screw the bolt into it, or goof up opening a coffee or shortening can with the key on the metal strip and need to pull the metal strip off the can, pliers are the tool that will do it.

Montgomery Ward & Co.
619 W. Chicago Ave.
Chicago, Ill. 60607

Sears, Roebuck & Co.
925 S. Doman Ave.
Chicago, Ill. 60607

Nasco
1524 Princeton Ave.
Modesto, Ca. 95352

PLOWS

In order to seed a field with vegetables or grass or clover, etc., you must first have a plow to turn the soil. There are plows you push yourself for small garden plots all the way up to the huge tractors used by commercial growers. They all operate on the same principle, though: cutting and breaking up the ground. There are anti-plow viewpoints, but I am not a follower of them.

PLOW + SHARES

Montgomery Ward & Co.
619 W. Chicago Ave.
Chicago, Ill. 60607

Sears, Roebuck & Co.
925 S. Doman Ave.
Chicago, Ill. 60607

Mother's General Store Catalog
Box 506
Flat Rock, N.C. 28731

POST HOLE DIGGER

There are two types of post hole diggers. One is the auger type, which you turn and twist down into the ground, pulling it out to empty the dirt as the auger fills with earth. There is also the the type with two handles fastened on two sort of shovels which you thrust down into the earth, then pinch closed and pull out of the earth. Either one requires an effort to use, but unless the ground is very hard or full of stones, a post hole can be dug in a short time.

POST HOLE DIGGER

91

POSTHOLE DIGGER (Cont'd)

Berstein Bros. Co.
100 N. Mechanic St.
Pueblo, Colo. 81003

Nasco
1524 Princeton Ave.
Modesto, Ca. 95352

Montgomery Ward & Co.
619 W. Chicago Ave.
Chicago, Ill. 60607

Sears, Roebuck & Co.
925 S. Doman Ave.
Chicago, Ill. 60607

POWER PLANTS

A good thing to have if you have no other source of electricity or don't wish that other source! Power plants large enough to operate just about anything electric you can think of are made. You can have a deep freeze or washer, television, etc. You may want a gas refrigerator and cook stove and have a power plant which would provide lights, television, sewing

POWER PLANT

machine, radio, iron, etc. Prices vary from reasonably low for what you get in return, to incredibly high.

Onan Co.
2515 University Ave. S.E.
Minneapolis, Minn. 55414

Kohler Co.
Kohler, Wis. 53044

PRAYING MANTIS

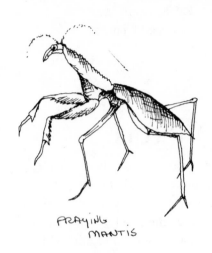

PRAYING MANTIS

A rather spooky looking insect of the family Mantidae, order Orthoptera. In other words, these are very odd looking green bugs that eat a tremendous amount of insects per day. These are very beneficial to the home gardener. I understand they eat caterpillers, etc. Praying mantises are also beneficial in the greenhouse.

Montgomery Ward & Co.
619 W. Chicago Ave.
Chicago, Ill. 60607

PRESSES, CIDER

CIDER PRESS

These are well made presses for making cider and are made of special materials so as not to give your juice any unpleasant flavor. If you desire, you can also press grapes for wine making as well. There are several sizes of presses made.

Guinta Bros.
1035 Christian
Philadelphia, Pa. 19147

Mirro Aluminum Co.
1516 Washington St.
Manitowoc, Wis. 54220

Mother's General Store Catalog
Box 506
Flat Rock, N.C. 28731

Sears, Roebuck & Co.
925 S. Doman Ave.
Chicago, Ill. 60607

Edward Renneburg Sons, Inc.
2635 Boston St.
Baltimore, Md. 21224

PRESSES, LARD/FRUIT

PRESSES, LARD/FRUIT

We used one of these for making apple cider this fall and it worked great! We first ground up the apples in the food grinder and then pressed the ground apples. If you form an assembly line (some cutting the apples, some grinding and some pressing and bottling the juice) it really goes fast. I was quite amazed at how much juice you get for a small amount of fruit.

Giunta Bros.
1035 Christian
Philadelphia, Pa. 19147

Mother's General Store Catalog
Box 506
Flat Rock, N.C. 28731

Mirro Aluminum Co.
1516 Washington St.
Manitowoc, Wis. 54220

Sears, Roebuck & Co.
925 S. Doman Ave.
Chicago, Ill. 60607

PULLEYS

This simple tool can become a very important and necessary tool. If you install combinations of fixed and moveable pulleys, you can move things that weigh many times more than you do. The pulley consists of a wheel

SCREW PULLEY

PULLEYS (Cont'd)

with a grooved rim where the rope runs and a frame where the wheel turns freely on an axle. There may be more than one wheel on the frame (block).

Berg Evans Chain Co.
110-T S.E. Main St.
Portland, Ore. 97214

Herter's Inc.
Waseca, Minn. 56093

Jeffrey Mfg. Co.
956 N. Fourth St.
Columbus, Ohio 43216

E. F. Marsh Engineering Co.
14 Hanley Industrial Ct.
St. Louis, Mo. 63144

PUSH LAWN MOWER

Personally, I'm more for turning the sheep in on the lawn (they water, mow and fertilize it with no effort on your

LAWN MOWER

part) but sometimes this isn't always feasible. So if you do have to mow the lawn, a good sharp push lawn mower works just fine. I remember in a book that is one of my favorites, the part where the kids mow the lawn and also teach a foreign gentleman to mow the lawn (kind of Tom Sawyer and the fence type thing). When you finish, a big ice cold glass of lemonade sounds pretty great. Needless to say these are one man or child mowers!

American Lawn Mower Co.
Muncie, Ind.

Great States Corp.
P.O. Box 369
Shelbyville, Ind. 46176

Montgomery Ward & Co.
619 W. Chicago Ave.
Chicago, Ill. 60607

Sears, Roebuck & Co.
925 S, Doman Ave.
Chicago, Ill. 60607

Southland Mower Co., Inc.
P.O. Box 347
Selma, Ala. 36701

QUILTING FRAMES

My wife says she tried putting a quilt top on a queen sized quilt on the living room floor and sure wished she had a quilting frame. Surprisingly, they are not as terribly expensive as one thinks they might be. They are also beautifully constructed and, although they do take up space, it sure beats moving out half the furniture and crawling all over the floor for hours on end! They are

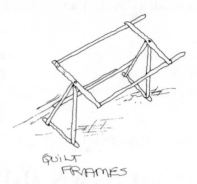

QUILT FRAMES

adjustable so you can make any size quilt from crib size up. There are also smaller quilting frames which are suitable for large quilts or even smaller pieces of needlework, approximately 1.8" x 27".

Lee Wards
1200 St. Charles Rd.
Elgin, Ill. 60120

Sears, Roebuck & Co.
925 S. Doman Ave.
Chicago, Ill. 60607

Montgomery Ward & Co.
619 W. Chicago Ave.
Chicago, Ill. 60607

RAKE, FIRE

This useful tool, while being great for fighting fires, can be used for clearing weeds, underbrush, banks, ditches, etc.

RAKE, FIRE

Nasco
1524 Princeton Ave.
Modesto, Ca. 95352

RAZOR STROPS

Besides being a good thing with which to paddle bottoms in Grandpa's day, this is what kept the man of the house's razor sharp. I remember as a kid, a friend of mine's dad was a barber, and watching him strop his razor was really something. It looked  as though he was going to cut off a finger any minute, but he never did! His razor was really sharp, too—he used to test it by cutting a hair. (Probably for show for us kids.)

Illinois Razor Strap Co.
865 N. Sangamon Ave.
Chicago, Ill. 60622

Morris Flamingo, Inc.
80 East Gate Dr.
Danville, Ill. 61832

Mother's General Store Catalog
Box 506
Flat Rock, N.C. 28731

Pearlduck, Inc.
97-35 Allendale St.
Jamaica, N.Y. 11435

RAZOR, WIND UP (MONACO SHAVER)

Some friends of ours introduced this item to us. The Monaco wind up razor is the answer to an electric razor without electricity. The company states that this kind of razor was on the Appolo 14 space flight and kept the astronauts clean shaven for the entire trip. The friends who introduced this razor to us took it on vacation with them and found it very satisfactory. One sort of neat feature is that it is self-sharpening!

Haverhills
584 Washington St.
San Francisco, Ca. 94111

RIVETS

This short, soft metal bolt with a head on one end is used to join many objects together such as metal plates, leather, and pockets on the famous Levis. There are several shapes of rivets such as flat head, button head, countersunk button head and boiler rivet.

Albany Products Co.
916 American St.
San Carlos, Ca. 94070

Nasco
1524 Princeton Ave.
Modesto, Ca. 95352

Milford Rivet & Machine Co.
Pacific Division
12945 E. Imperial Hwy.
Santa Fe Springs, Ca. 90670

Vulcan Rivet & Bolt Corp.
1020 Pinson St.
Birmingham, Ala. 35217

RIVET SETTERS/MACHINES

This is the machine used to set or hammer the rivet into place. There are several sizes made for home and shop use.

Mother's General Store Catalog
Box 506
Flat Rock, N.C. 28731

Nasco
1524 Princeton Ave.
Modesto, Ca. 95352

RIVETING MACHINE + RIVETS

ROPE SPLICER & SLICER

ROPE SPLICER

ROPE SLICER

A very useful and money saving tool. Repair, cut, or splice together your broken ropes. Some splicers are sold with instructions showing you how to make different splices, which would be a great help.

Miller Stockman
P.O. Box 5407
Denver, Colo. 80217

SACK NEEDLES

SACK NEEDLES

This is a curved needle used for closing burlap bags, etc. Haven't seen them in years. If you sack up walnuts, grain, etc., this would be a handy tool to have.

Barr Bros. Co.
770 Reed St.
Santa Clara, Ca. 95050

SADDLES

There are lots of different types of saddles, both ready made and made to your order. There are also the "bareback pads" suitable for light riding. The very ornate western saddles can be tooled all over and have silver placed on them, while your racing saddles are very plain and light, having no excess weight.

SADDLES

Miller Stockman
P.O. Box 5407
Denver, Colo. 80217

Montgomery Ward & Co.
619 W. Chicago Ave.
Chicago, Ill. 60607

SADDLE SOAP

SADDLE SOAP

This is suitable for cleaning any leather article from saddles to shoes, belts, etc. Clean your leather boots with saddle soap and then apply neatsfoot oil to give your clean boots a waterproof coating.

Nasco
1524 Princeton Ave.
Modesto, Ca. 95352

Sears, Roebuck & Co.
925 S. Doman Ave.
Chicago, Ill. 60607

SAW, BOW PRUNING TUBULAR STEEL

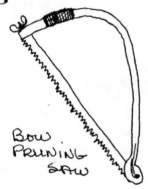

BOW PRUNING SAW

A saw with a curved handle and a straight blade, shaped somewhat like the letter D. This type saw allows heavy sawing in a limited space, although the saw itself is quite lightweight. I've used it to pinch hit for a meat saw and it works fine.

Herter's Inc.
Waseca, Minn. 56093

Montgomery Ward & Co.
619 W. Chicago Ave.
Chicago, Ill. 60607

Nasco
1524 Princeton Ave.
Modesto, Ca. 95352

SAW, BUCK

Basically a one-man saw used for bucking logs, which means cutting the logs into rounds. If you don't have a chain saw, there is almost no other way to cut rounds except with a large two-man crosscut saw.

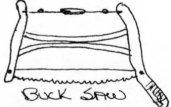

BUCK SAW

SAW, BUCK (Cont'd)

It's important to keep the turnbuckle on the top at the proper position in order to keep the blade taut.

John H. Graham & Co., Inc.
617 Oradell Ave.
Oradell, N.J. 07649

True Temper Corp.
1623 Euclid Ave.
Cleveland, Ohio 44115

Pennsylvania Saw Corp.
305 Hill — P.O. Box 1303
York, Pa. 17405

SAW, CROSSCUT

A two-man saw, usually quite large. It, like the buck saw, can be used to saw

CROSS CUT SAW

rounds, but this saw can also be used to actually fell a tree. Its use in cutting down trees is a little tricky, since it tends to bind after cutting halfway through the tree.

Atkins Saw Div.
1825 N. Theobold Extd.
Greenville, Miss. 38701

Great Neck Saw Manufactures, Inc.
Mineola, N.Y. 11501

Curtis Saw Division of Jemco Tool Corp.
Towers Bldg.
Seneca Falls, N.Y. 13148

SCRAPERS, BARN

SCRAPERS, BARN

This is another multi-use tool from Nasco. It's got a reversible blade, allowing it double life-time. Although it's called a barn scraper, you could clean any hard surface, such as snow from paved (or frozen!) driveways, sidewalks, etc. You can also scrape the floors of any barn, be it sheep, cattle or whatever— also chicken houses, etc.

Nasco
1524 Princeton Ave.
Modesto, Ca. 95352

SCYTHES

This is a one-man powered scythe, not the machined type. There are several kinds of blades available for scythes: brush, grass and weeds. The scythe snaths are made of wood or aluminum.

John H. Graham Co., Inc.
617 Oradell Ave.
Oradell, N.J. 07649

Mother's General Store Catalog
Box 506
Flat Rock, N.C. 28731

Nasco
1524 Princeton Ave.
Modesto, Ca. 95352

True Temper Corp.
1623 Euclid Ave.
Cleveland, Ohio 44115

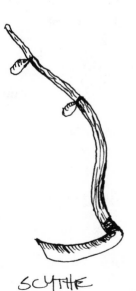

SCYTHE

SHEARS, LARGE

A very useful thing to
own. A good sharp pair
of large sized shears
comes in handy when
cutting items such as
canvas, denim, upholstery
material or even carpet
Keep them sharp though.

SHEARS

Nasco
1524 Princeton Ave.
Modesto, Ca. 95352

SHEEP SHEARS, HAND

When you have a few sheep to be sheared, you can handle
the job fine with simple
hand shears. Also, there
isn't always electricity
available at all times or
in all places where you
may have to shear. They
aren't awfully expensive
to purchase. The shears
make great grass shears if
you give out on the sheep business or convert to powered
shears. We find the hand shears adequate for giving "O.B.
hair cuts" before lambing.

SHEEP SHEERS

Columbian Cutlery Co.
P.O. Box 123
Reading, Pa. 19603

Mendocino County Farm Supply
2200 N. State St.
Ukiah, Ca. 95482

John H. Graham & Co., Inc.
617 Oradell
Oradell, N.J. 07649

Nasco
1524 Princeton Ave.
Modesto, Ca. 95352

Hawker Siddeley Inc.
7 T Delaware Dr.
Lake Success, N.Y. 11040

SICKLE/TRIMMER

TRIMMER
OR
SICKLE

Used for trimming grass and brush by hand, or you can cut small amounts of feed for livestock or poultry.

Mother's General Store Catalog
Box 506
Flat Rock, N.C. 29731

G. E. Ruhmann Mfg. Co.
801 N. Main
Schulenburg, Tex. 78956

True Temper Corp.
1623 Euclid Ave.
Cleveland, Ohio 44115

SIEVES/FRUIT & VEGETABLE PRESS

This cone shaped sieve can be used in many, many ways. My wife uses it for ricing potatoes, sieving squash or pumpkin for pies, making applesauce, running berries through (which removes most of the seeds). There's a wood pestle which is made to fit the sieve, and by merely operating the pestle in a circular motion the sieve is in operation. It's a great tool for running tomatoes through to remove seeds and skin for tomato sauce, paste, juice, etc. She says she couldn't think of doing without it.

SIEVE

Mother's General Store Catalog
Box 506
Flat Rock, N.C. 28731

Sears, Roebuck & Co.
925 S. Doman Ave.
Chicago, Ill. 60607

SKIN/FUR STRETCHERS

When tanning or curing hides, stretching them is very necessary. Fur stretchers are made for shaping the pelt while it is drying. There are different sizes available for skunk, fox, raccoon, opossum, mink, muskrat, etc. These also help prevent over-stretching of the hide.

FUR STRETCHER

Gander Mountain, Inc.
P.O. Box 248
Wilmot, Wis. 53192

Herter's Inc.
Waseca, Minn. 56093

SLEIGH KIT

This is a "tool" for romanticists more than anything else. This kit converts a pony cart, or any cart, to a sleigh quickly. Imagine riding through the countryside after a big snow, wrapped snug in blankets and with jingle bells on your harness. When you grumble about how cold it would be, etc., re-

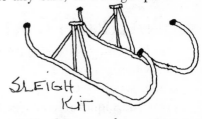

SLEIGH KIT

member, you're showing your age! The kit may also come in handy if there was an emergency after a snowfall and normal transportation was cut off. Ah well, I just had to include it in the book!!

Nasco
1524 Princeton Ave.
Modesto, Ca. 95352

SMOKER (FISH, FOWL, MEAT)

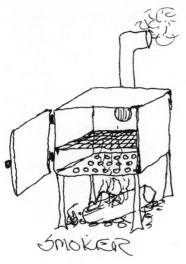

This is a portable smoker which Herter's came up with after apparently a bit of effort on their part. They recommend that you use certain woods for smoking meat, among which are apple wood, maple and hickory wood. Some meats mentioned which are smoked with success are pork, venison, bear and beef. Herter's say that approximately 50 hours of smoking time can be obtained from five pounds of wood chips. This smoker operates on 110 volt A.C. electricity. Of course you can build your own because good plans are abundant, but I've never seen one more effective than this electrical one.

Herter's Inc.
Waseca, Minn. 56093

SNAKEBITE KITS

The low cost of a snakebite kit if you are way back into the wilderness may be a life saver. I understand certain physicians would rather you only apply a tourniquet if you are 20 or 30 minutes away from medical aid, but if you are really out in the wilderness this tiny kit will fit in  your pocket and isn't bothersome to carry, so perhaps you might think about getting one or checking the condition of your old one.

Herter's Inc.
Waseca, Minn. 56093

SNOWSHOES

While I've never been in snow deep enough to require snow-

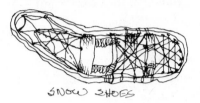

SNOW SHOES

shoes, I have been in snow deep enough to tire you out wading through it! I understand they really work well and that there are some specially designed with bindings which allow the beginner to maneuver with no problems. Snowshoes are made of several materials. There are the wood and rawhide kind as well as the polypropylene ones.

Herter's Inc.
Waseca, Minn. 56093

SOIL TEST KITS

Garden, grass, field crops, etc., won't grow? Maybe there is something lacking in your soil. We had a patch of ground in our garden this year where even weeds wouldn't grow. We are all set now for next spring with

SOIL TEST KIT

a soil test kit! Most test kits make numerous tests for phosphorus, nitrogen, acidity and potash. Prices vary, but if you are having trouble, it is certainly worth the investment.

Herter's Inc.
Waseca, Minn. 56093

Montgomery Ward & Co.
619 W. Chicago Ave.
Chicago, Ill. 60607

Mother's General Store Catalog
Box 506
Flat Rock, N.C. 28731

Nasco
1524 Princeton Ave.
Modesto, Ca. 95352

SPADES

SPADE

This is a very obvious tool, but I felt it should be included as there are a number of varieties and it may be of some help to someone.
Let's start with a soil sampling spade. I'd never heard of this one myself! Made especially for taking soil samples, enabling you to

SPADE

test the soil. Now to just name a few others, there are general purpose spades, balling and root pruning spades, commercial round point spades, drain spades, floral spades, transplanting spades and square point blade spades. There may be more, but I wasn't able to locate them.

Montgomery Ward & Co.
619 W. Chicago Ave.
Chicago, Ill. 60607

Sears, Roebuck & Co.
925 S. Doman Ave.
Chicago, Ill. 60607

Nasco
1524 Princeton Ave.
Modesto, Ca. 95352

SPOKE SHAVERS

A blade with two handles, one on each side. The blades are replaceable. They are used for making spokes (at least originally). They

SPOKE SHAVE

are more precise than a plane and can be used to shave edges and corners of wood. Also good for shaving off the edges on uneven boards of a barrel so that the stays fit more tightly.

Stanley Tool Div.
666 Myrtle St.
New Britain, Conn. 06053

SPRAYERS

If you feel it necessary to spray your orchards, garden, barns, road sides or whatever, there are any number of

HAND SPRAYER

kinds of sprayers to do the trick. Compressed air hand sprayers have a small tank and are very suitable for small areas. There are also large compressed air sprayers. The back pack or the knapsack sprayers are several gallons larger. Then there are the large, tractor drawn ones, more suitable for large farms or orchards, etc.

Montgomery Ward & Co.
619 W. Chicago Ave
Chicago, Ill. 60607

Nasco
1524 Princeton Ave.
Modesto, Ca. 95352

SPREADER, ROTARY BROADCASTER (HAND) FERTILIZER

This is a hand operated (push type) fertilizer spreader which is inexpensive, yet can be used on quite a large area. It broadcasts in 4 to 8 foot swaths, which allows a big area to be covered in a fairly short time. This would be a great help to the person who wants to farm fairly large but just hasn't a lot of money for a big commercial rig.

SEED BROADCASTER

Sears, Roebuck & Co.
925 S. Doman Ave.
Chicago, Ill. 60607

SPRING SCALE

I realize this isn't necessarily the correct name for this scale.

It is the kind we had from the time I was a kid and this is what my dad called it. I see it listed as a fisherman's scale in one catalog. At any rate, this type of scale hangs by a ring and is rectangular in shape. It weighs things up to 25 or 50 or 100 or 200 or 300 pounds. There is a hook on the bottom where whatever you are weighing is hung.

SPRING
SCALE

Herter's Inc.
Waseca, Minn. 56093

Nasco
1524 Princeton Ave.
Modesto, Ca. 95352

SQUEEZE CHUTES, PORTABLE

Several of these allow for one man operation. It also allows you to brand or treat an animal anywhere you desire or can be installed anywhere you prefer. The chute holds cattle or horses immobile so they may be examined or treated.

SQUEEZE CHUTE

Berstein Bros.
100 N. Mechanic St.
Pueblo, Colo. 81003

Nasco
1524 Princeton Ave.
Modesto, Ca. 95352

110

STANCHIONS

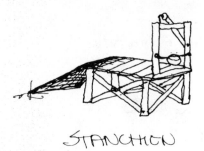

STANCHION

Useable in either metal or wood stalls, these ready built stanchions are really great. Saves time and effort in trying to build one, and if there is any other way to milk a goat comfortably, I haven't found it.

Nasco
1524 Princeton Ave.
Modesto, Ca. 95352

Sears, Roebuck & Co.
925 S. Doman Ave.
Chicago, Ill. 60607

STERNO STOVES

A power failure (or out of propane) and no other way to to cook? A Sterno stove would be the thing to have. You could at least heat water, warm a baby's bottle, heat soup, at any rate get by until the power was restored. They take very little space as they fold flat for storage.

STERNO STOVE

Sterno, Inc.
300 Park Ave.
New York, N.Y. 10022

STOCK PRODS

When loading or moving cattle, a stock prod enables you to

STOCK PROD

do it faster and easier. Useable on other livestock as well. They are battery powered and don't really need to be used much after the

animal experiences it. They don't really hurt the animal but livestock sure respect them.

Nasco
1524 Princeton Ave.
Modesto, Ca. 95352

Weston Mfg. & Supply Co.
Box 16297
Denver, Colo. 80216

STOCK TANKS

I found galvanized steel
stock watering tanks come
in sizes from 47 gallons up
to 19,035 gallons. Quite a
range in sizes! The larger
ones come in corrugated
or flat sheet galvanized
steel. They are also made

STOCK TANKS

of 22, 20, 12 and 10 gauge galvanized steel, depending on
size and price.

Berstein Bros.
100 N. Mechanic St.
Pueblo, Colo. 81003

Montgomery Ward & Co.
619 W. Chicago Ave.
Chicago, Ill. 60607

STONE, BENCH

This is the same as the oil stone mentioned before in this

BENCH STONE

book, the difference being in
the size. The bench stone is
a larger size. It has its own
wooden storage box, and
from the size, I'd venture to
say one in a lifetime would
probably do for the average
person.

Gander Mountain, Inc.
P.O. Box 248
Wilmot, Wis. 53192

STRAIGHT RAZOR KITS

There may be a lot of outlets for this product but I couldn't locate them. You don't see them that often except in barber shops. For the brave at heart of the older gentleman on your "hard to buy for" gift list this has to be the answer. It's not everyone who owns one, that's for sure.

Mother's General Store Catalog
Box 506
Flat Rock, N.C. 28731

STRAIGHT
RAZOR

SUGAR BUCKETS, PINE

PINE BUCKET

If you are involved with maple sugar you know about these. They are beautiful buckets with bow handle and lid all made of pine. You can store yarn, fruit, hobby craft supplies, scarves, anything you want in these neat buckets. They come in various sizes and are a great buy for the price.

Weston Bowl Mill
Weston, Vt. 05161

SUNDIAL

Love these! Not very useful on a rainy day, but great on clear days. They are a great addition to the beauty of a garden. You really can tell time by them too! This is probably one of the oldest timepieces, dating back to ancient Egypt. The difference between mean time (clock) and solar time (sundial) is correlated by use of standard tables. A correction is  also made for the difference between longitude of sundial and local standard meridian.

Mother's General Store Catalog
Box 506
Flat Rock, N.C. 28731

Sundial & More
P.O. Box H
Playground Rd.
New Ipswich, N.H. 03071

SWATTER, FIRE

This is effective for small brush, grass, etc., fires. It is made of a 12 by 15 inch piece of rubber-treated belting. One uses it like a fly swatter.

Nasco
1524 Princeton Ave.
Modesto, Ca. 95352

TACK TRUNKS, HORSEMAN'S

TACK TRUNKS, HORSEMAN'S (Cont'd)

This beautifully made trunk is really made to hold your saddle, bridle, etc. It's quite nicely made and there's no reason you couldn't store blankets, linens, etc., in it for the home.

Montgomery Ward & Co.
619 W. Chicago Ave.
Chicago, Ill. 60607

TAGGER (NASCO TRIGGER OPERATED GUN)

TAGGER

This name brand tagger works in three steps to help you tag your livestock for easy identification. The three steps are (1) load gun needle with the tag, (2) pierce the animal's ear, and (3) pull trigger, inserting and positioning tag. Nice if you have a lot of tagging to do.

Montgomery Ward & Co.
619 W. Chicago Ave.
Chicago, Ill. 60607

Nasco
1524 Princeton Ave.
Modesto, Ca. 95352

TANKS, REDWOOD WATER

If you have a spring (or pump up to a holding tank), a redwood tank would be the best kind to have. Redwood outlasts most metal tanks and it also outlasts most other kinds of wood as well. Most companies ship these tanks knocked down. Assembly is quite easy.

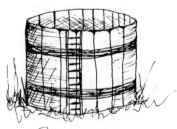

REDWOOD WATER TANKS

Mendocino County Farm Supply
2200 N. State St.
Ukiah, Ca. 95482

Montgomery Ward & Co.
619 W. Chicago Ave.
Chicago, Ill. 60607

TANNING EQUIPMENT

TANNING EQUIPMENT

It's fun to tan hides from the deer you get during hunting season or animals that have been trapped. It's not especially a hard job, but it is time consuming. Tanning hides, cutting them up and making vests, moccasins, hat bands, bed spreads, etc., is a great exercise in patience, but if you have ever seen a well made rabbit-skin bed spread, it's not hard to be motivated.

Herter's Inc.
Waseca, Minn. 56093

TARPS

A tarp is a bit like I mentioned with burlap bags—when you need one, nothing else will do the job. You can use tarps in many ways, from covering hay to covering whatever you are handling in your pick-up bed and want to protect. You can also cover farm equipment during bad weather.

TARPS

TARPS (Cont'd)

Herter's Inc.
Waseca, Minn. 56093

Montgomery Ward & Co.
619 W. Chicago Ave.
Chicago, Ill. 60607

Nasco
1524 Princeton Ave.
Modesto, Ca. 95352

Sears, Roebuck & Co.
925 S. Doman Ave.
Chicago, Ill. 60607

TOASTER, CAMP, 4 SLICE

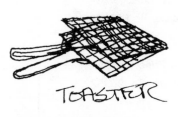

TOASTER

I remember these from when I was little. They really work well. The low price makes them even nicer to own. They are not for the absent minded, though.

Gander Mountain, Inc.
P.O. Box 248
Wilnot, Wis. 53192

Herter's Inc.
Waseca, Minn. 56093

TORTILLA PRESSES

A real easy way to make fresh tortillas any time you want. I don't know if you save money making your own, but 10 pounds of masa harina isn't very expensive. My wife says you add one third cup flour and one cup water to one and three-fourths cups masa harina for one dozen

TORTILLA PRESS

corn tortillas. She warns to be sure to place waxed paper under and on top of your little ball of masa harina in your press or you'll never be finished scraping off your stuck tortillas! The bag of masa harina has directions as well as a Mexican cookbook.

Fanal
Monterey, Mexico   will this address do anyone any good?

TRANSIT/FARM LEVEL

TRANSIT FARM
LEVEL

If you know how to survey,
there are many fine level-
transits available. I admit the
prices are high, but you can't
get precision instruments
cheaply. If you need one,
though, you need one.

Montgomery Ward & Co.
619 W. Chicago Ave.
Chicago, Ill. 60607

Nasco
1524 Princeton Ave.
Modesto, Ca. 95352

TRAPS, HAV-A-HART

If you've a pesty animal and
don't wish to kill it but want
to catch it and remove it, the
"Hav-A-Hart" traps work
well. They are a take-off on
the box traps where the animal is taken alive and un-
harmed. Well constructed of

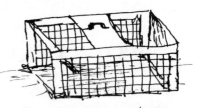

TRAPS, HAVE-A-HART

sturdy mesh and sheets of galvanized steel, and there are
several sizes available.

Gander Mountain, Inc.
P.O. Box 248
Wilnot, Wis. 53192

Herter's Inc.
Waseca, Minn. 56093

Mother's General Store Catalog
Box 506
Flat Rock, N.C. 28731

Nasco
1524 Princeton Ave.
Modesto, Ca. 95352

TRAP, RAT & MOUSE

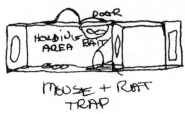

MOUSE + RAT TRAP

Rats and mice are trapped without harm in this cage. As they try to reach the bait, they fall through a trap door which closes behind them. The whole trap is made of No. 2 heavy galvanized wire cloth.

Mother's General Store Catalog
Box 506
Flat Rock, N.C. 28731

TRAPS, SPARROW

This is a trap that doesn't kill the birds that enter it, and is made by "Hav-a-Hart" company. There are birds which are known pests and are destructive to many crops. They can be caught and destroyed humanely and innocent birds and protected birds removed alive and free.

SPARROW TRAP

Herter's Inc.
Waseca, Minn. 56093

TRAPS, VARMINT

These are usually single coil, double coil and long spring

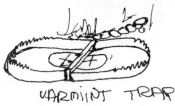

VARMINT TRAP

traps. They are set by trappers who are usually trapping for furs. There is usually bait placed somewhere near the top area to help lure the animal. These traps are used for muskrat, mink, rabbits, weasel, pocket and striped gophers, opossum, skunk, raccoon, fox, badger, beaver, otter, coyote, lynx, bobcat, etc.

119

TRAPS, VARMINT (Cont'd)

Gander Mountain, Inc.
P.O. Box 248
Wilnot, Wis. 53192

Herter's Inc.
Waseca, Minn. 56093

Mother's General Store Catalog
Box 506
Flat Rock, N.C. 28731

Nasco
1524 Princeton Ave.
Modesto, Ca. 95352

VETERINARY SUPPLIES

A very necessary thing when operating a farm or ranch no matter what size. There is almost always a call for some article, no matter how small. You need not buy a great deal of supplies, especially since you may never use many of them, but the vaccines (used annually) and syringes and balling guns can be purchased with reasonable assurance that they will be used.

VET SUPPLIES

Nasco
1524 Princeton Ave.
Modesto, Ca. 95352

Sears, Roebuck & Co.
925 S. Doman Ave.
Chicago, Ill. 60607

Weston Mfg. & Supply Co.
Box 16297
Denver, Colo. 80216

WASH BOARDS

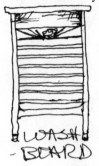

It isn't often you use a wash board any more, but the year our washer went out there was many a raw knuckle around our house. I discovered I had two kinds: a metal surface and a glass surface. The glass one hurts less to scrub on. You wouldn't believe how tired your hands and back can get! They do work, though. Wash boards are a must in any jug band, too!

Columbus Washboard Co.
1372 Oxley Rd.
Columbus, Ohio 43212

Mother's General Store Catalog
Box 506
Flat Rock, N.C. 28731

National Washboard Co.
1217 Florida St.
Memphis, Tenn. 38106

Wabash, Inc.
1217 Florida St.
Memphis, Tenn. 38106

WATER BOWL,
NON-SIPHONING (LIVESTOCK)

This is a specially designed water bowl that meets US Public Health recommendations. It's made so that the water will not siphon back into your water supply and thereby contaminate it. Made of stainless steel.

Montgomery Ward & Co.
619 W. Chicago Ave.
Chicago, Ill. 60607

Sears, Roebuck & Co.
925 S. Doman Ave.
Chicago, Ill. 60607

121

WATER WHEELS

WATER WHEEL

The water wheel is almost as old as man himself. Whether by gravity or pressure, they were used to harness water power primarily for grinding grain. Connected to a generator, they make a great source of free hydro-electricity.

Brewer & Taylor Foundry, Inc.
Rome, Ga. 30161

James Leffel & Co.
Springfield, Ohio 45501

WEATHER VANES

WEATHERVANES

Need to know the direction of the wind from inside your house? These look really good on the barn or mounted on a pole in your front yard. There are many designs of weather vanes. Some places even custom design and make the weather vanes to order.

WEATHER VANES (Cont'd)

Florida Aluminum Casting Foundry, Inc.
2705 Division Ave.
West Palm Beach, Fla. 33407

Herter's Inc.
Waseca, Minn. 56093

Kenneth Lynch & Sons
172 Factory Rd.
Wilton, Conn. 06897

Nasco
1524 Princeton Ave.
Modesto, Ca. 95352

Western Fire Equipment Co.
440 Valley Dr.
Brisbane, Ca. 94005

WEDGES

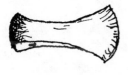

MAUL

These tools are used when falling or splitting wood. They help prevent pinching or binding your chain saw. They are made of aluminum or a very strong kind of plastic, steel or magnesium. Just pay for a new chain guide because you bent your old one and you will become a wedge fan!

WEDGE

Dixie Industries, Inc.
1210 Greenwood Ave.
Chattanooga, Tenn. 37404

Foster Aluminum Alloy Products Corp.
4151 Adetha St.
Forestville, N.Y. 14062

Nasco
1524 Princeton Ave.
Modesto, Ca. 95352

Warwood Tool Co.
North 19th St.
Wheeling, W.Va. 26003

WELL WHEEL
(DRAWS UP BUCKET)

Fastened by a hook to a
frame built over your well,
this device is what the rope
goes through to aid in
drawing up the bucket.
Made of cast iron, it is
quite attractive as well as
durable.

WELL WHEEL

Durbin-Durco, Inc.
1430 Woodson Rd.
St. Louis, Mo. 63132

King Div.
500 Hicks Rd.
Palatine, Ill. 60067

Lodge Manufacturing Co.
P.O. Box 380
South Pittsburg, Tenn. 37380

Power Tools, Inc.
510 S. Hicks Rd.
Palatine, Ill. 60067

WHEELBARROWS

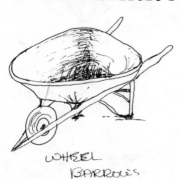

WHEEL
BARROWS

Several kinds of wheelbarrows
are made, and some are designed to handle much easier
than others. Very useful when
transporting small, heavy or
awkward loads around your
farm. They are particularly
useful for removing wet manure from your barn.

Montgomery Ward & Co.
619 W. Chicago Ave.
Chicago, Ill. 60607

Nasco
1524 Princeton Ave.
Modesto, Ca. 95352

WHIPS, BUGGY

For show or actual use, these small,
well made buggy whips are still available.
I've seen them used to train horses.
Their "snap" is worse than their bite.

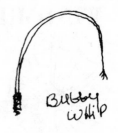

Buggy Whip

Nasco
1524 Princeton Ave.
Modesto, Ca. 95352

Sears, Roebuck & Co.
925 S. Doman Ave.
Chicago, Ill. 60607

WHIPS, BULL

A very long and heavy whip which takes a lot of practice
to use. The crack of a bull whip
sounds like a rifle shot. They
used to be used for hobbling
calves or cows. You snap this
long whip into the cow's hind
legs, tangling the animal. It can
also be used for snapping branch-
es off trees and even snapping
pistols out of people's hands!

Bull Whip

Nasco
1524 Princeton Ave.
Modesto, Ca. 95352

WINCHES

Useful for lifting heavy loads
or just moving a heavy object
around. I've used them often
for pulling engines out of my
trucks or even for lifting
1100 lb. carcasses for gutting
and skinning.

Winch

Nasco
1524 Princeton Ave.
Modesto, Ca. 95352

WINDMILLS

wind mill

A very economical way to obtain water. Pump into a large holding tank when the wind blows and use from the tank whether the wind is blowing or not. If you live where you get wind daily, you should be able to use a windmill. Attach an old car alternator and voltage regulator to one and get some free electricity.

Aeromotor Division
Broken Arrow, Okla. 74012

Berstein Bros. Co.
100 N. Mechanic St.
Pueblo, Colo. 81003

Dempster Industries, Inc.
Box 848
Beatrice, Neb. 68310

Heller-Aller Co.
Napoleon, Ohio 43545

WIRE ROLLER

Ever roll up barbed wire? Came out of it mighty full of holes, huh? This device not only rolls wire up, but lays wire as well. Handy if you're building a large amount of fence. You can roll or lay smooth or barbed wire much faster with one of these.

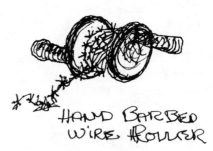

HAND BARBED WIRE ROLLER

Montgomery Ward & Co.
619 W. Chicago Ave.
Chicago, Ill. 60607

Nasco
1524 Princeton Ave.
Modesto, Ca. 95352

Sears, Roebuck & Co.
925 S. Doman Ave.
Chicago, Ill. 60607

WIRE STRETCHER

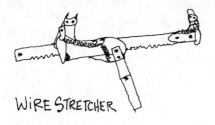

WiRE STRETCHER

Takes up slack in sagging fence wires, and thus prevents livestock from getting out. Most of the stretchers that I located are one-man operated and are easy to use.

Nasco
1524 Princeton Ave.
Modesto, Ca. 95352

WOODEN BOWLS

An infinity of uses in the kitchen. These are a great buy compared to most prices because Weston Bowl Mill not only sells the regular perfect bowls, they also sell seconds at great prices. If you have any ambition, always try to purchase wooden bowls unfinished. The price difference is worth the small amount of sanding required and the oil treatment afterwards.

WOODEN BOWLS

Weston Bowl Mill
Weston, Vt. 05161

WOODEN CRADLES

Next best thing after pacifiers to quiet babies. Pacifiers are not recommended by doctors these days, so it's back to wooden cradles. Although not used very long (children soon outgrow them) they are a beautiful addition to the nursery.

WOODEN CRADLES

Hydor-Therme Corp.
7200 Airport Hwy.
Pennsauken, N.J. 08110

127

WOODEN PEGS

If you are a wood hobbyist, these may be the pegs you've been looking for to peg instead of dowel or nail your pieces together. You can use them for several things, such as making a key holder of your own design, up to putting together house framing.

WOODEN PEGS

American Woodworking Co.
Box 335-T
Montello, Wis. 53949

Brown Wood Products Co.
200 Northfield Rd.
Northfield, Ill. 60093

E. B. Estes & Sons
98 Fifth Ave.
New York, N.Y. 10011

WOODEN TOYS
(TOPS, YOYOS, ETC.)

WOODEN TOYS

These are some of the most beautiful wood toys being made today. The ones I've listed aren't painted. Plain wood and really incredible! There are trucks, stick horses and a Gee-Haw Whimmydiddle! How about that?

Mother's General Store Catalog
Box 506
Flat Rock, N.C. 28731

Weston Bowl Mill
Weston, Vt. 05161

128

WOOD WINDOW STOP

This device has got to be one of the
most clever. It's so simple it makes you
feel stupid for not thinking of it yourself! No more windows falling down
when your back is turned, scaring
everyone to death. I won't tell you
anymore. Just get Weston Bowl Mill
catalog and be surprised!

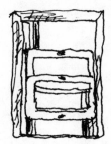

WOOD WINDOW
STOP

Weston Bowl Mill
Weston, Vt. 05161

YOKES, OXEN

NECK YOKE

For those still using oxen for plowing.
Frankly, I've never seen them in use,
but you can also use them to hang
planters from for a yard decoration.

Milling Forging Co.
P.O. Box 516T
Lansing, Mich. 48903

Mich Craft Corp.
19997 19-Mile Rd.
Big Rapids, Mich. 49307

PRODUCT LIST

ADZES — 1
ALTERNATORS, PTO
  driven — 2
ANTI-freeze for cabin
  toilets — 2
ANVILS — 3
APPLE peelers — 3
AUGER, earth/ice/wood — 4
AWLS, piercing and stiching
  — 4
AXES — 5
AXE, brush — 6
BAGS, burlap — 6
BALL peen hammers (see
  Hammers, ball peen)
BARBEQUE grills (see Grills,
  barbeque)

BARN scrapers (see Scrapers,
  barn)
BARRELS, pine/oak — 7
BASKET, steak — 8
BEAN pot & stand, cast
  iron — 8
BEAR traps — 9
BEES/bee keeping equip-
  ment — 9
BELLOWS, hand — 10
BELLS, cow/goat/sheep/
  turkey — 11
BELLS, farm & school
  master's — 11
BELL scraper — 12
BENCH stone (see Stone,
  bench)

131

BINS, grain — 13
BIRDHOUSES — 13
BLINDS (see Bridle blinds)
BOOT jacks — 14
BOTTLE capper — 15
BOTTLE caps — 15
BOTTLE corkers — 16
BOTTLE cutter — 16
BOTTLE lifter — 17
BOTTLE openers — 18
BOWLS (see Wooden bowls)
BRANDING irons, heat/
    electric/freeze — 18
BRIDLE blinds — 19
BROADCASTERS (see Hand
    broadcasters)
BROODERS, chicken — gas/
    electric/woodburning — 20
BRUSH axe (see Axe, brush)
BRUSH cutter, motorized
    — 20
BUCKBOARDS & carts — 21
BUCKETS (see Sugar buckets,
    pine)
BUCK saw (see Saw, buck)
BUGGY whips (see Whips,
    buggy)
BUILDINGS, portable — 21
BULL whips (see Whips, bull)
BURLAP bags (see Bags,
    burlap)
BUTCHER blocks — 22
BUTTER churns — 22
BUTTER molds (see Molds,
    butter)
CALF puller — 23
CANDLERS (see Egg candlers)
CANNING kettles — 24

CAN sealer — 24
CANTHOOKS (see Peavies
    & canthooks)
CAPPERS (see Bottle cappers)
CARTS (see Buckboards &
    carts)
CASTRATORS — 25
CATTLE guards — 26
CATTLE scale — 26
CHAIN saw files & sharpener
    — 27
CHICK brooders (see Brooders,
    chicken)
CHURNS (see Butter churns)
CIDER presses (see Presses,
    cider)
COFFEE mill grinder — 27
COME-along — 28
COMPOSTING bins — 29
CONCRETE mixers — 29
CORKERS (see Bottle
    corkers)
CORN planters — 30
CORN sheller/walnut huller
    — 30
COULTERS & shares, plow
    — 31
COUNTRY wine additive
    kit — 31
CRADLES, wood (see Wood
    cradles)
CREAM cans — 32
CREAM separators — 32
CROCKS — 33
CROSSCUT saw (see Saw,
    crosscut)

MEASURING wheel, land
   — 80
MEAT grinders (see Grinders,
   meat)
MEAT saw, hand — 81
MILK pails (see Pails, milk)
MILK strainer — 81
MILLS (see Coffee mills,
   Grain mills, etc.)
MOLDS, butter — 82
MOUSE traps (see Traps,
   rat & mouse)
MUZZLES, wire — 83
NEATSFOOT oil — 83
NEEDLES (see Sack needles)
NOSE bags — 83
NOTCHER (see Ear notcher)
NUTCRACKERS, cast iron/
   wood — 84
OIL stones — 84
PACK saddles — 85
PAILS, milk/dairy — 86
PEAVIES & canthooks — 86
PEELERS, apple (see Apple
   peelers)
PEELING bars — 87
PEGS (see Wooden pegs)
PHONOGRAPH, battery
   operated — 87
PICKS — 88
PIG (see Hog)
PIPE threaders — 88
PLANES, wood — 89
PLIERS, fence — 89
PLIERS, general purpose — 90

PLOWS — 91
   (see also Coulters & shares,
   plow)
POPCORN popper (see Fire-
   place popcorn popper)
POST hole digger — 91
POTS (see Bean pot & stand,
   cast iron)
POTATO digger (see Digger,
   potato)
POWER plants — 92
PRAYING mantis — 93
PRESSES, cider — 93
PRESSES, lard/fruit — 94
PRESSES, tortilla (see Tortilla
   presses)
PULLEYS — 94
PUMPS (see Hand pumps)
PUSH lawn mower — 95
PRODS (see Stock prods)
PRUNING saw (see Saw, bow
   pruning)
QUILTING frames — 96
RACKS (see Food drying
   racks)
RAKE, fire — 96
RASPS (see Files/rasps)
RAZOR kits (see Straight
   razor kits)
RAZOR strops — 97
RAZOR, wind up (Monaco
   shaver) — 97
RIVETS — 98
RIVET setters/machines — 98
ROPE splicer & slicer — 99

SACK needles (see also Bags, burlap) – 99
SADDLES – 99
SADDLE soap – 100
SAW, bow pruning – 100
SAW, buck – 100
SAW, meat (see Meat saw)
SAWS, crosscut – 101
SCALE (see Spring scale)
SCALES, cattle (see Cattle scales)
SCALES, dairy (see Dairy scales)
SCALES, egg (see Egg grader/scales)
SCOOP (see Grain scoop)
SCRAPER (see Foot scraper)
SCRAPERS, barn – 102
SCYTHES – 102
SEED broadcasters (see Hand seed broadcasters)
SEPARATORS, cream (see Cream separators)
SHARES (see Coulters & shares, plow)
SHEARS, large – 103
SHEEP shears, hand – 103
SICKLE/trimmer – 104
SIEVES/fruit & vegetable press – 104
SKIN/fur stretchers – 105
SLEDGE hammers (see Hammers, sledge)
SLEIGH kit – 105
SLING (see Hay sling)
SMOKER (fish, fowl, meat) – 106

SNAKEBITE kits – 106
SNOWSHOES – 107
SOIL test kits – 107
SPADES – 108
SPARROW traps (see Traps, sparrow)
SPOKE shavers – 108
SPRAYERS – 109
SPREADER, rotary broadcaster (hand) fertilizer – 109
SPRING scale – 110
SQUEEZE chutes, portable – 110
STANCHIONS – 111
STERNO stoves – 111
STOCK prods – 111
STOCK tanks – 112
STONE, bench – 112
STONES, oil (see Oil stones)
STRAIGHT razor kits – 113
STROPS (see Razor strops)
SUGAR buckets, pine – 113
SUNDIAL – 114
SWATTER, fire – 114
TACK trunks, horseman's – 114
TAGGER (Nasco trigger operated gun) – 115
TANKS, redwood water – 115
TANNING equipment – 116
TARPS – 116
TOASTER, camp, 4 slice – 117
TORTILLA presses – 117

LIST OF COMPANIES

Acme Metal Goods Mfg. Co.
2 Orange St.
Newark, N.J. 07102

Aeromotor Div.
Broken Arrow, Okla. 74012

Alabama Bag & Burlap Co.
4330 Powell Ave. S.
Birmingham, Ala. 35222

Alaska Freezer Co., Inc.
Winchendon, Mass. 01475

Albany Products Co.
916 American St.
San Carlos, Ca. 94070

American Handicrafts
1312 Mission St.
San Francisco, Ca. 94103

American Lawnmower Co.
Muncie, Ind.

American Leather Co.
1609 Tampa St.
Tampa, Fla. 33601

American Lightning Rod Co.
P.O. Box 82033
Lincoln, Neb. 68501

American Woodworking Co.
Box 335-T
Montello, Wis. 53949

Atkins Saw Div.
1825 N. Theobold Extd.
Greenville, Miss. 38701

Atlanta Bag Co.
S. 5th St. & Union Ave.
Brooklyn, N.Y. 11211

Atlantic Service Co., Inc.
711 Caton Ave.
Brooklyn, N.Y. 11218

Atlas Rigging Supply Corp.
181-J Vanderpool St.
Newark, N.J. 07114

Augusta Bag & Burlap Co.
Augusta, Ga.

Ayotte's Designery
Box 287
*Center Sandwich, N.H. 03227

W. H. Bagshaw Co., Inc.
25 Pine St.
Nashua, N.H. 03060

Bay State Abrasives Div.
15 Union St.
Westborough, Mass. 01581

Bazaar de la Cuisine
1003 2nd Ave.
New York, N.Y. 10022

The Bee Hive
Dept. G.F.
Ojai, Ca. 93023

H. Behrens Mfg. Co.
471 W. Third St.
Winona, Minn. 55987

Berg Evans Chain Co.
110-T S.E. Main St.
Portland, Ore. 97214

Bergen Arts & Crafts, Inc.
Box 381
Marblehead, Mass. 01945

Berman Leather Co.
147 South St.
Boston, Mass. 02111

Bernstein Brothers Co.
100 N. Mechanic St.
Pueblo, Colo. 81003

Bertels Metal Ware Co., Inc.
Rutter & Garner
Kingston, Pa. 18704

Bevin Bros. Mfg. Co.
Bevin Rd.
East Hampton, Conn. 06424

John Blue Co.
Laurinburg, N.C. 28352

Bob's Arts & Crafts, Inc.
11880 N. Washington St.
Northglenn, Colo. 80233

Boin Arts & Crafts Co.
87 Morris St.
Morristown, N.J. 07960

Bogart & Hopper, Inc.
111 Charlotte Pl.
Englewood Cliffs, N.J. 07632

Braun North American
55 Cambridge Parkway
Cambridge, Mass. 02142

Brewer & Taylor Foundry, Inc.
Rome, Ga. 30161

Brown & Bigelow
1286 University Ave.
St. Paul, Minn. 55104

Brown Wood Products Co.
200 Northfield Rd.
Northfield, Ill. 60093

Brunner & Lay
9300 W. King
Franklin Park, Ill. 60131

Buck Knives, Inc.
1717 N. Magnolia Ave.
El Cajon, Ca. 92021

Buffalo Hammer Mill Corp.
1243 McKinley Parkway
Buffalo, N.Y. 14218

Buffalo Forge Co.
465 Broadway
Buffalo, N.Y. 14204

G. A. Burbridge Co.
1031 Richmond
Houston, Tex. 77006

Butcher Block and More
6100 S. Clinton St.
Chicago, Ill. 60616

Candle Mill Village
Peterbrook, Inc.
East Arlington, Vt. 05252

Capewell Division
Stanadyne, Inc.
61 Governor St.
Hartford, Conn. 06106

Champion Blower & Forge, Inc.
100 W. Central Park
Roselle, Ill. 60172

Chief Products Co.
701 E. 59th
Los Angeles, Ca. 90001

Cherry Burrell Corp.
7515 N. Lindar Ave.
Skokie, Ill. 60076

Chromaly American Corp.
160 Fifth Ave.
New York, N.Y. 10011

Cleveland Leather Co.
2824 Lorain Ave.
Cleveland, Ohio 44113

Clinton Products
South Tecumseh Rd.
Clinton, Mich. 49236

Cole Mfg. Co.
1318 Central
Charlotte, N.C. 28205

Collins Machinery Corp.
951-55 Monterey Pass Rd.
Monterey Park, Ca. 91754

Colo Craft
1310 S. Broadway
Denver, Colo. 80210

Columbian Cutlery Co.
P.O. Box 123
Reading, Pa. 19603

Columbus Washboard Co.
1372 Oxley Rd.
Columbus, Ohio 43212

Continental Can Co., Inc.
Beverage Div.
5745 E. River Rd.
Chicago, Ill. 60631

Countryside General Store
Rt. 1, Box 239
Waterloo, Wis. 53594

Cornwall Corp.
500 Harrison Ave.
Boston, Mass. 02118

Countryside General Store
Rt. 1, Box 239
Waterloo, Wis. 53594

Cross Imports, Inc.
210 Hanover St.
Boston, Mass. 02113

Cumberland General Store
Rt. 3, Box 479
Crossville, Tenn. 38555

Curtis Saw Div. of Gemco
   Tool Corp.
Towers Bldg.
Seneca Falls, N.Y. 13148

Decker Mfg. Co.
300 Blondeau St.
Keokuk, Iowa 52632

Delkor Industries, Inc.
Talmadge at 29th Ave. S.E.
Minneapolis, Minn. 55414

Dempster Industries, Inc.
Box 848
Beatrice, Neb. 68310

Dick Blick Co.
P.O. Box 1267
Galesburg, Ill. 61401

Dixie Industries, Inc.
1210 Greenwood Ave.
Chattanooga, Tenn. 37404

Dixon Williams, Inc.
752 Washington Ave.
Carlstadt, N.J. 07072

Douglas Homs Corp.
1542 Industrial Way
Belmont, Ca. 94002

Durbin Durco, Inc.
14300 Woodson Rd.
St. Louis, Mo. 63132

Du-Well Mfg. Co.
W. Greenfield & S. 41st
Milwaukee, Wis.

E. F. Marsh Engineering Co.
14 Hanley Industrial Ct.
St. Louis, Mo. 63144

Easy Speed Co.
1171 Folsom at Rodgers
San Francisco, Ca. 94103

Empire Coffee & Tea Co.
486 Ninth Ave.
New York, N.Y. 10028

E. B. Estes & Sons
98 Fifth Ave.
New York, N.Y. 10011

Everedy Co.
200 Monroe Ave.
Fredrick, Md. 21701

Everhot Mfg. Co.
Flothow & St. Charles
Maywood, Ill. 60153

The Fairbanks Co.
10 Glenwood Ave.
Binghamton, N.Y. 13902

Fairfield Industries, Inc.
336 Fairfield Rd.
Fairfield, N.J. 07006

Fanal
Monterey, Mexico

Farnham Equipment Div. of
   Lisk Savory Corp.
1167 Clinton St.
Buffalo, N.Y. 14240

Fay & Egan Co.
2024 Eastern Ave.
Cincinnati, Ohio 45202

Filpaco Industries, Inc.
3837 W. Lake St.
Chicago, Ill. 60624

Florida Aluminum Casting
   Foundry, Inc.
2705 Division Ave.
West Palm Beach, Fla. 33407

Forrest Jones, Inc.
3274 Sacramento St.
San Francisco, Ca. 94115

Foster Aluminum Alloy Products
   Corp.
4151 Adeltha St.
Forestville, N.Y. 14062

Freeman Supply Co.
5720 Harvey Wilson Dr.
P.O. Box 15381
Houston, Tex. 77020

Freund Can Co.
167 W. 84th St.
Chicago, Ill. 60620

Fuller Mfg. Co.
Centerville, Iowa 52544

Gander Mountain, Inc.
P.O. Box 248
Wilmot, Wis. 53192

Gibralter Equipment & Mfg. Co.
P.O. Box 304K
Alton, Ill. 62002

Giunta Bros.
1035 Christian
Philadelphia, Pa. 19147

Goodell Co.
Antrim, N.J.

John H. Graham & Co., Inc.
617 Oradell Ave.
Oradell, N.J. 07649

Graver Tank & Mfg. Co.
9200 E. Flair Dr.
El Monte, Ca. 91731

Great States Corp.
P.O. Box 369
Shelbyville, Ind. 46176

The Greenery
Box 489
Soquel, Ca. 95073

Grey Iron Casting Co.
P.O. Box 40
Wrightsville, Pa. 17368

Great Neck Saw Mfg., Inc.
Mineola, N.Y. 11501

Griedman Bag Co.
801 E. Commercial
Los Angeles, Ca. 90012

Hammel Riglander Co., Inc.
423-435 Hudson St.
New York, N.Y. 10014

The Handcrafters
1 W. Brown St.
Waupon, Wis. 53962

Handcrafted Wood
P.O. Box 425S
Aptos, Ca. 95003

Handy-Walden, Inc.
50-13 47th Ave.
Woodside, N.Y. 11377

Harper Trucks, Inc.
P.O. Box 33
Wichita, Kan. 67201

Hastings Equity Grain Bin
  Mfg. Co.
E. Hastings, Neb. 68901

Haverhill's
584 Washington St.
San Francisco, Ca. 94111

Hawker Siddeley, Inc.
7T Delaware Dr.
Lake Success, N.Y. 11040

Heller-Aller Co.
Napoleon, Ohio 43545

Herrschner's, Inc.
Hoover Rd.
Stevens Point, Wis. 54481

Herter's, Inc.
Waseca, Minn. 56093

The Hidden Village
215 Yale Ave.
Claremont, Ca. 91711

H & H Tool Co.
Box 430-B
Montebello, Ca. 90640

J. F. Hodgkins Co.
Randolph
Gardiner, Me. 04345

Homestead Industries
2014 Los Angeles Ave.
Berkeley, Ca. 94707
and
General Delivery
Argenta, B.C., Canada

House of Yarn & Crafts
Rt. 1, Lafayette Rd.
Seabrook, N.H. 03874

Hubbard Tool Division
6305 Butler St.
Pittsburg, Pa. 15201

Hussey Enterprises, Inc.
801 S. Ohio
Martinville, Ind. 46151

Hydor-Therme Corp.
7200 Airport Hwy.
Pennsauken, N.J. 08110

Illinois Pure Aluminum Co.
109 Holmes
Lemont, Ill. 60439

Illinois Razor Strap Co.
865 N. Sangamon Ave.
Chicago, Ill. 60622

Indiana Leather Supply
R.R. 2, Box 103
Bloomington, Ind. 47401

International Edge Tool Co., Inc.
565 Eagle Rock Ave.
Roseland, N.J. 07068

James Liffel & Co.
Springfield, Ohio

Jeffery Mfg. Co.
956 N. 4th St.
Columbus, Ohio 43216

Kenneth Lynch & Sons
172 Factory Rd.
Wilton, Conn. 06897

Kershaw Mfg. Co.
P.O. Box 9328
Montgomery, Ala. 36108

Kessenich
7463 Harwood Ave.
Wauwatosa, Wis. 53213

King Div.
500 Hicks Rd.
Palatine, Ill. 60067

Kline, Savidge Co., Inc.
163 N. 3rd St.
Philadelphia, Pa. 19106

Klein, Mathias & Son, Inc.
7200 McCormick Rd.
Chicago, Ill. 60645

Kohler Co.
Kohler, Wis. 53044

K M Yarn Co.
24065 West Ten Mile Rd.
Southfield, Mich. 48075

Oscar Krenz, Inc.
Ashby Ave. & 6th St.
Berkeley, Ca. 94710

Leach Co.
2737 Harrison
Oshkosh, Wis. 54901

Lekvar by the Barrel
968 Second Ave.
New York, N.Y. 10022

Leetonia Tool Co.
Holt & Main Ave.
Leetonia, Ohio 44431

Lee Wards
1200 St. Charles Rd.
Elgin, Ill. 60120

Lily Mills Co.
P.O. Box 88
Shelby, N.C. 21850

Lixie Div.
P.O. Box 5048
Esmond, R.I. 02917

Lodge Mfg. Co.
P.O. Box 380
South Pittsburg, Tenn. 37380

Louisville Tin & Stove Co.
737 S. 13th St.
Louisville, Ky. 40210

Lyon Electric Co.
3425 Hancock
P.O. Box 81303B
San Diego, Ca. 92110

Mac Leather Co.
424 Broome St.
New York, N.Y. 10013

MacMillan Arts & Crafts, Inc.
9520 Baltimore Ave.
College Park, Md. 20740

MacPherson Bros.
730 Polk St.
San Francisco, Ca. 94109

Maid of Scandinavia
3244 Raleigh Ave.
Minneapolis, Minn. 55416

Robert G. Main & Sons
Tomley & Gaffle Rd.
Wycoff, N.J. 07481

Manganaro Foods
488 Ninth Ave.
New York, N.Y. 10018

141

A. Mamaux & Son
Mamaux Bldg.
Pittsburg, Pa.

Matticks Mfg. Co.
Matticks Bldg.
6415 E. Compton Blvd.
Paramount, Ca. 90723

McGregor Greenhouses
Box 36510
Santa Cruz, Ca. 95063

Metal Products Corp.
45 W. 19th St.
Weehawken, N.J. 07087

Miller Stockman
Box 5407
Denver, Colo. 80217

Milwaukee Tool & Equipment
   Co., Inc.
2775 S. 29th St.
Milwaukee, Wis. 53246

Mendocino County Farm Supply
2200 N. State St.
Ukiah, Ca. 95482

Metalspecialties, Inc.
1383 Kings Hwy.
Fairfield, Conn. 06430

Metle-Pres, Inc.
Foot of Commerce St.
Wilmington, Del. 19801

Fred Meyer of California, Inc.
14 Park Ave.
Emeryville, Ca. 94608

Mick Craft Corp.
19997   19 Mile Rd.
Big Rapids, Mich. 49307

Milford Rivet & Machine Co. —
   Pacific Div.
12945 E. Imperial Hwy.
Santa Fe Springs, Ca. 90670

Miller Franklin, Inc.
34 Meadow St.
East Orange, N.J. 07017

Miller Stockman
8500 Zuni, Box 5407
Denver, Colo. 80217

T. J. Miller & Co.
201 13th S.E.
Washington, D.C. 20003

Milling Forging Co.
P. O. Box 516T
Lansing, Mich. 48903

Mills Thomas Mfg. Co.
2182 Bennett Rd.
Philadelphia, Pa. 19116

Milwaukee Tool & Equipment
   Co., Inc.
2775 S. 29th St.
Milwaukee, Wis. 53215

Mirro Aluminum Co.
1516 Washington St.
Manitowoc, Wis. 54220

Mission Foundry & Stove Works
544 Treat Ave.
San Francisco, Ca. 94110

Montgomery Ward & Co.
619 W. Chicago Ave.
Chicago, Ill. 60607

Morris Flamingo, Inc.
80 East Gate Dr.
Danville, Ill. 61832

Mother's General Store Catalog
Box 506
Flat Rock, N.C. 28731

C. T. Moyse & Son
P.O. Box 228-T
E. Rockaway, N.Y. 11518

Paul Mueller Co.
P.O. Box 828
Springfield, Mo. 63101

Nasco
1524 Princeton
Modesto, Ca. 95352

National Poultry Equip.
615 Wells Ave. N.
Benton, Wash. 98055

National Washboard Co.
1217 Florida St.
Memphis, Tenn. 38106

Natural Leather
203 Bleeker St.
New York, N.Y. 10012

Nicholson File Co.
Providence, R.I.

Northwestern Coffee Mills
217 N. Broadway
Milwaukee, Wis. 53202

Norton Co.
50 New Bond St.
Worcester, Mass. 01606

Ohaus Scale Corp.
35 Hanover Rd.
Florham Park, N.J. 07932

Oley Tooling, Inc.
Oley, Pa. 19547

Olson Mfg. Co.
620 S. Broadway
Albert Lea, Minn. 56007

Onan Co.
2515 University Ave. S.E.
Minneapolis, Minn. 55414

C. S. Osborne & Co.
Warren St.
Harrison, N.J. 07029

Osmundson Mfg. Co.
Perry, Iowa 50220

Pacific Coast Greenhouse Mfg. Co.
430 Burlingame Ave.
Redwood City, Ca. 94063

Pack-O-Fun
14 Main St.
Park Ridge, Ill. 60068

Pancoast International Corp.
120-22 Liberty St.
New York, N.Y. 10006

Paprikas Weiss
1546 Second Ave.
New York, N.Y. 10028

Paragon Steel & Tool Co., Inc.
134 Rt. 20
E. Rutherford, N.J. 07073

Paramount Wire Products
1035 Westminster Ave.
Alhambra, Ca. 91803

The Peaney Mfg. Co.
Box 371
Brewer, Me. 04412

Pearlduck, Inc.
97-35 Allendale St.
Jamaica, N.Y. 11435

L. F. Pease Co.
19 Gosvenor Ave.
East Providence, R.I.

F. B. Pease Co., Inc.
E. Henrietta & Jefferson
Rochester, N.Y. 14620

Pennsylvania Saw Corp.
305 Hill
P.O. Box 1303
York, Pa. 17405

Peter Reimuller Greenhouseman
P.O. Box 2666 J10
Santa Cruz, Ca. 95063

Portage Tool Co.
2675 Wingate at Cemetery
Akron, Ohio 44314

J. E. Porter Co.
Ottawa, Ill. 61350

Portland Stove Foundry Co.
57 Kennebec
Portland, Me. 04101

Power Tools, Inc.
510 S. Hicks Rd.
Palatine, Ill. 60067

Presque Isle Wine Cellars
9449 Buffalo Rd.
North East, Pa. 16428

Rasmussen Iron Works, Inc.
12028 E. Philadelphia
Whittier, Ca. 90601

J. G. Read Bros.
101 21st St.
Ogden, Utah 84401

142

Redwood Domes
Div. SK
Aptos, Ca. 95003

Arthur W. Reed Machine Co.
900 Thayer
Little Rock, Ark. 72202

Reliable Strainer Mfg. Co.
1725 N. Eastern Ave.
Los Angeles, Ca. 90032

Edward Renneburg Sons Co.
2635 Boston St.
Baltimore, Md. 21224

Riverside Tent & Awning Co., Inc.
3226 Franklin Ave.
Riverside, Ca. 92507

Rife Hydraulic Eng. Mfg. Co.
Box 367-T
Milburn, N.J. 07041

Robbins Incubator Co.
2555 S. Santa Fe Dr.
Denver, Colo. 80223

Robbins Lighting Protection Co.
124-A East 2nd St.
Maryville, Mo. 64468

Ro-Mark Mfg. Co.
7009 Florin Perkins Rd.
Sacramento, Ca. 95828

R & R Mill Co.
45 W. First North
Smithfield, Utah 84335

Rowe Automatic Can Sealer
820 Saratoga Lane
Buffalo Grove, Ill. 60090

G. E. Ruhmann Mfg. Co.
801 N. Main
Schulenburg, Tex. 78956

Sacramento Bag Mfg. Co.
530 Q St.
Sacramento, Ca. 95814

The Salem Craftsmen's Guild
3 Alvin Place
Upper Montclaire, N.J. 07043

Scientific Filter & Machinery Co.
342 Canal St.
New York, N.Y. 10013

Screw Conveyor Corp.
704 Hoffman St.
Hammond, Ind. 46320

Sherrill Mfg. Co.
Rt. 5, Box 175
Cullman, Ala. 35055

Sav Mor Leather Supply
1409 S. Los Angeles St.
Los Angeles, Ca. 90015

Sax Arts & Crafts
P.O. Box 2002
Milwaukee, Wis. 53201

Sears, Roebuck & Co.
925 S. Koman Ave.
Chicago, Ill. 60607

Semplex of USA
4805 Lyndale Ave. N.
Minneapolis, Minn. 55412

The Shelby Mfg. Co.
400 Sigler St.
Sidney, Ohio 45365

M. Siegel Co., Inc.
186 South St.
Boston, Mass. 02111

Simonds Saw & Still Div.
Interwale & Mack Rd.
Fitchburg, Mass. 01420

Simosen Metal Products Corp.
11600 W. King
Franklin Park, Ill. 60131

Sioux Steel Co.
1961/4 E. 6th St.
Sioux Falls, S.D. 57103

Sjogren Tool & Machine Co., Inc.
Auburn, Mass 01501

Skill Crafts Div., The Brown
Leather Co.
205 Virginia Ave.
Joplin, Mo. 64801

Snow & Neally Co.
Bangor, Me. 04401

So-Rite Mfg. & Supply Co.
P.O. Box 6097
Raleigh, N.C. 27608

Southland Mower Co., Inc.
P.O. Box 347
Selma, Ala. 36701

Southwest Mfg. Co.
P.O. Box 722
Downey, Ca. 90241

Spaulding & Frost & Co.
Fremont, N.H. 03044

S & S Arts & Crafts
Colchester, Conn. 06415

S. T. Leather Co.
329-33 E. Long St.
Columbus, Ohio 43215

Stained Glass Club
482 Tappan Rd.
Northwale, N.J. 07647

Stanley Tools Division
666 Myrtle St.
New Britain, Conn. 06053

Star Hydraulics, Inc.
2729 Clinton St.
River Grove, Ill. 60171

Star Mfg. Co.
Carpentersville, Ill. 60110

Sterno, Inc.
300 Park Ave.
New York, N.Y. 10022

Stone Mfg. & Supply Co.
1212 Kansas Ave.
Kansas City, Mo. 64127

Sundial & More
P.O. Box H
Playground Rd.
New Ipswich, N.H. 03071

Sunstream Bee Supply

Tacoma Hive Mfg. Co.

Tandy Leather Co.
1001 Foch St.
Fort Worth, Tex. 76107

Titan Tool Supply Co., Inc.
66 Comet Ave.
Buffalo, N.Y. 14216

Toijalan Kardetehdas
P L 25 37801
Toijala, Finland

Toledo-Beaver Tool Co.
1445 Summit St.
Toledo, Ohio

Tools of the Trade
RFD
Fair Haven, Vt. 05743

Townsend Mfg. Co., Inc.
Lake Wales, Fla. 33853

True Temper Corp.
1623 Euclid Ave.
Cleveland, Ohio 44121

Saml. Underberg, Inc.
620 Atlantic Ave.
Brooklyn, N.Y. 11217

The Union Fork & Hoe Co.
500 Dublin Ave.
Columbus, Ohio 43215

The Unique
21½ E. Bijou
Colorado Springs, Colo. 80902

United States Crown Corp.
100 Oak St.
Norwood, N.J. 07648

Universal Container Corp.
540 Madison Ave.
New York, N.Y. 10022

USM Corp.
Dept. 28, 140 Federal St.
Boston, Mass. 02110

Varpa — Looms Ltd.
Osmontie 35
46800 Myllykooski
Finland

Village Candle & Craft
Box 486
Marshfield, Wis. 54449

Voos Cutlery, Inc.
101 Jermis St.
Cheshire, Conn. 06410

Vulcan Corp.
6 E. 4th
Cincinnati, Ohio 45202

Vulcan Rivet & Bolt Corp.
1020 Pinson St.
Birmingham, Ala. 35217

Wabash, Inc.
1217 Florida St.
Memphis, Tenn. 38106

Wagner Specialty Co.
1647 Dodge
Burlington, Wis. 53105

Waltham Grinder Wheel
Waltham, Mass. 02154

Warren Tool Div.
P.O. Box 68
Hiram, Ohio 44234

Warwood Tool Co.
North 19th St.
Wheeling, W.Va. 26003

Weavers Corner Studios
P.O. Box 125
Kendall, Fla. 33156

Western Botanical Co.
710 Wilshire Blvd.
Santa Monica, Ca. 90401

Western Fire Equip. Co.
440 Valley Dr.
Brisbane, Ca. 94005

Weston Bowl Mill
Weston, Vt. 05161

Weston Mfg. & Supply Co.
Box 16297
Denver, Colo. 80216

White River Industries
915 Pine
Muskegon, Mich. 49440

White Mt. Freezer Co.
Lincoln Ave.
Winchendon, Mass. 01475

The Whole Mother Earth Water
   Works
Green Spring, W.Va. 26722

Wiese Corp.
1501 Fifth St.
Perry, Iowa 50220

Wisconsin Cheese Makers Guild
6048 W. Beloit Rd.
Milwaukee, Wis. 53219

Wisner Mfg. Co.
1165 Globe Ave.
Mountainside, N.J. 07092

Woodings-Verona Tool Works
Thomas St.
Verona, Pa. 15147

Worcester Wire Novelty Co., Inc.
111 Timonium Rd. W.
Timonium, Md.

OLIVER PRESS

Presents

the

Finder's Guide Series

FINDER'S GUIDE No. 1

Joseph Rosenbloom

This book offers the do-it-yourselfer a complete directory of companies and equipment available for many diversified projects and plans. This indexed directory solves the problem of finding out "who" makes "what." There is something here for every taste and level of skill.

288 pp   January, 1974
LC 73-92459 $3.95

Kits and Plans for the Budget Minded

CRAFT SUPPLIES SUPERMARKET

FINDER'S GUIDE No. 2

Joseph Rosenbloom

A well illustrated and indexed directory of craft supplies. Thousands of products, including materials, kits, tools, etc., from over 450 companies, are analyzed from their catalogs.

224 pp, ill., August 1974
LC 74-84298 $3.95

THE COMPLETE KITCHEN

FINDER'S GUIDE No. 3

Anne Heck

This book is a comprehensive guide to hard-to-find utensils, and describes the companies supplying such utensils as well as giving information about their catalogs. Many illustrations of unusual or interesting utensils.

96 pp, ill., September, 1974
LC 74-84299 $2.95

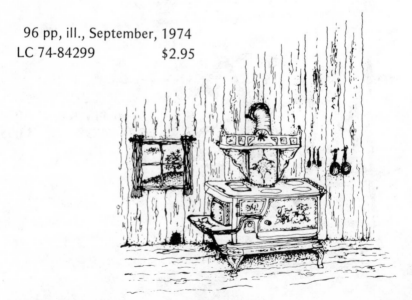

HOMEGROWN ENERGY

FINDER'S GUIDE No. 4

Power for the Home and Homestead

Gary Wade

This book offers the do-it-yourselfer a very complete directory to thousands of available products involved in the production of home grown power. Water wheels, solar cells, windmills, methane generators and other exotic equipment and parts are covered and indexed in depth.

96 pp, ill., September, 1974
LC 74-84300 $2.95

SPICES, CONDIMENTS, TEAS, COFFEES, AND OTHER DELICACIES

FINDER'S GUIDE No. 6

Roland Robertson

Answers difficult questions involved with finding and purchasing unusual ingredients, beverages and foods which are difficult to obtain locally. This illustrated and indexed directory is highly browsable, to say nothing of gastronomically stimulating.

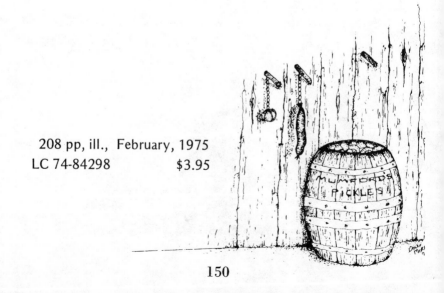

208 pp, ill., February, 1975
LC 74-84298 $3.95

ᴛʜᴇ Scribner Library

America's Quality Paperback Series
CHARLES SCRIBNER'S SONS
Shipping and Billing Departments
Vreeland Ave., Totowa, New Jersey 07512

Order Blank

Dear Sirs:

I believe your new series "FINDER'S GUIDES" fills a
definite need for information and I would like to order:

QUANTITY	TITLE	TOTAL
	copies of KITS AND PLANS @ $3.95 ea.	
	copies of CRAFT SUPPLIES SUPERMARKET @ $3.95 ea.	
	copies of THE COMPLETE KITCHEN @ $2.95 ea.	
	copies of HOMEGROWN ENERGY @ $2.95 ea.	
	copies of SPICES, CONDIMENTS, TEAS, COFFEES, AND OTHER DELICACIES @ $3.95 ea.	
	copies of COUNTRY TOOLS @ $3.95 ea.	
	copies of ALL OF THE ABOVE BOOKS ($21.70 Total)